HIDDEN MIND

A JOURNEY OF RECONNECTION

Tom Griffin and Dr Nuala Bent
Foreword by Professor Jan deVries

Published by Biosciences 2015

Copyright © 2015 Tom Griffin and Dr Nuala Bent

Foreward by Professor Jan deVries, D.Sc

Cover design and Graphics by Krzysztof Daszynski

ISBN 978 - 0 - 9932867

Printed and bound in Ireland by KPS Printing. Knock, Co Mayo

To order copies of this book or to find out more information about the Hiddenmind Bio-energy and Hiddenmind Investigative and Corrective Sound Program

or

For details of training courses visit:

www.hiddenmind.ie

HIDDEN MIND

A JOURNEY OF RECONNECTION

Tom Griffin and Dr Nuala Bent

BIOSCIENCES
Ireland & UK

Tom's Dedication

I dedicate this to the people who have inspired me most in my career in healing,
Zdenko Domancic, Ellen Eriksen, The Late Cameron Dawson,
The Late Dr. Josh Gilmore, The Late FR. Michael Lyons
and my Late brother Stephen Griffin.

Acknowledgements

My mother Kathleen, my wife Martina and my three children Avril, Andrew and Emily who gave me great support and encouragement. I would especially like to thank my brother Kevin for his invaluable work in editing and proof reading this book. I would like to thank Fr. Frank for proof reading,

I would like to thank Sylvia Henrich, Jeff McInreney, Valerie Dolan Miriam lynch, Kieran O'kelly, Brian McConway, Carmel and Enda Mooney, Tom Stensen, Ann Marie English, Ann Arnold, Vincent Murtagh, J.J Murphy, Maureen Murphy, Michael O Gara, Tina Forken and the support of all other therapists that I have trained over the last twenty five years.

I would like to thank all the people who contributed testimonies to this book.

And a special thanks to local media for their support
and encouragement over the years

A Special thanks to Krzysztof Daszynski
for his wonderful graphics and website design.

Nuala's Dedication

I dedicate this book to my Aunt the late Rita Millett
Remembering your generosity of Spirit, your support and above all, your humanity
Also remembering Andrew who touched our lives briefly and forever
– A reminder of the interconnectedness of it all

Acknowledgements

My children, Ian and Lisa for your support and encouragement.

Frank, for enduring the long conversations, and for your never waning support
and encouragement during work in progress.

Florence for her administrative skills and endurance.

My many friends, especially those who willingly indulged my passionate narratives

Tom who had complete faith in my ability to write and gave me
the opportunity to speak My Truth.

HIDDEN MIND FOREWORD

by Professor Jan deVries, D.Sc

I was greatly honoured to be asked to write a foreword for this very special book. It is undoubtedly a book that is far ahead of its time. The knowledge, science and ideas in the book are becoming more and more to the fore in today's world.

Today's society is completely different from the past. A lot more is questioned and there is a great need to understand more about life in general. If, in 60 years of practice, I have learned one thing, it is that energy plays a leading role in a healthy and happy life.

The writers of this book have delved deeply into their subjects and they have a wealth of experience between them. I have known Nuala Bent for many years. After an impressive career in academic research, she took early retirement to pursue her career in complementary therapies, and her passion is to raise awareness of the need for an integrated model of healthcare.

Over the years I had heard of Tom Griffin, who has been involved in energy healing for many years, but it was only recently that I met him for the first time. He is extremely well-known in the field of energy healing and has studied far and wide.

Their book "Hidden Mind", goes deeply into the realms of bio energy work and explains the special techniques that Tom has developed for those with special needs. From looking at the underlying causes of problems to specific corrections, the work could be described as ground-breaking and it will certainly make its mark in history.

Both Nuala's and Tom's mission, to elevate the human spirit through their practices in energy work and teaching methods, is nothing short of admirable.

Life is all about energy, and energy is all about life. I share with them the belief that much can be done to promote health if we know how to balance energy, and I am grateful to them for probing so deeply into this subject.

The human body is a microcosm in a macrocosm, and is therefore subject to all the physical, chemical and electrical laws. Recent moon proofs have shown that the earth has an iron sphere surrounding it, as well as an atmosphere. What happens in the iron sphere finally takes place in our atmosphere.

There is concern about what is happening to our protective ionosphere. The hydrogen and atomic bombs have ruptured this fine electro-magnetic energy field, which allows the ultraviolet and cosmic rays to come through, and in time this will injure our vegetation.

Naturally, the reader may ask what this has to do with the electro-magnetic fields of our bodies. It is important to remember that the body is an extension of the earth. We have three finer magnetic fields. When Nuala and Tom speak about vibrational healing, they are referring to a principal fact of the universe.

Every vibration is a movement in a particular direction at a specific rate. By vibrational healing we do not mean a discernible quiver or trembling movement, but those invisible health vibrations within the tissues of the body, which result in a similar vibration in the unconscious mind.

The human machine is composed of three parts: the skeleton with the ligaments, joints and muscles all controlled by the nerves; the great mind of humans- that gift that makes us potentially different from all fellow creatures; and the extremely delicate processing and manufacturing plants within the body designated as the viscera. This processing plant is designed to take in a variety of raw materials and convert them into products by the various components of the manufacturing division. These three parts are automatically welded into one functioning unit by the autonomous nervous system.

Life means movement and perfect form means rhythmic balance. All human bodies are built of atoms and it is this life force which maintains the normal rhythm. It is therefore very important that we balance the energies that keep us alive. There are billions of cells in a square inch of human tissue. These cells, every single one of them, have an inbuilt intelligence. They breathe and excrete waste matter and can even live independently of the human body, and indefinitely at that. This is a scientific fact.

All living matter has what we call a life force. It is this which distinguishes living forms. The mystery of life is really the mystery as to why and how a cell that is materially similar in every respect to a non-living cell, can continually discharge energy and produce evidence of life.

The vital life force or current flows to all fields and thus polarises them into active function. The ancients clearly understood that it was this vital force or chi energy which animates and controls the gross physical body functions.

As I said before, a human has three fields of bodies of action – physical, emotional and mental. A human being expresses energy every second. For every inhalation there must be an exhalation or the correct sequence of this polarity principle is broken. Short circuits in the body must be found and restored before health can really return. Structural polarisation by means of current flow is an important factor in health. Fields become obstructed by waste like carbon and acid deposits.

In every illness there is a lack of energy or life force in action. The finest therapy is that which balances the forces in the particular individual. Every molecule, every atom of this universe animates and vibrates. It is in constant vibration. Each minerals and each life cell in man, animal or insect, vibrates on its own frequency and wavelength. Also, there are vibrations of sound, colour, smell, heat and light.

In addition, the earth and all its living things are continuously being bombarded by stellar vibrations and cosmic rays of a frequency too high for us to comprehend. Furthermore, the earth is surrounded and criss-crossed by magnetic fields, man-made radio currents; all vibratory in nature. These are facts and governed by law. Vibrations of sound can cause pleasure or pain according to their effect on our emotions. The rhythmic tune will start out involuntary with a plaintive melody that can often bring a lump in the throat and tears to the eyes.

You will learn in this book why seeming miracles can be brought about with polarity balance and some of the mysteries of the hidden mind will be unravelled.

I am grateful to Nuala and Tom for writing this wonderful book. Through it, energy healing will reach a wider audience and I am quite sure we will all be richer for this in terms of our health and happiness.

Professor Jan deVries, D.Sc
Troon
Scotland

Tom Griffin - A History of Energy Healing

Tom has been involved in energy healing for almost thirty years. He had a background in philosophy and theology and developed an interest in healing. He became interested in Eastern philosophy and studied the Martial Arts and through this was introduced to Zdenko Domancic, a World famous Bio Energy healer. Tom trained with Zdenko twenty-five years ago in Croatia. Tom has popularised energy treatments through the medium of Bio-energy therapy and was the co-author of a best-selling book, "Bio Energy Healing - Therapy of the Future". He appeared on several television shows, and in numerous newspaper articles, national and international, testifying to the success of this therapy.

Tom and his colleague Michael O`Doherty set up the Plexus Bio Energy System to protect the identity of their specialised work. Tom has treated tens of thousands of people with a wide range of symptoms and diseases and has incorporated advanced bodywork programmes including the Harraga program and Vibrational Kinesiology into his work. He has also studied Tai-chi and Chi-Gung and is a third degree black belt in Martial Arts. Tom is also a Touch-For-Health Instructor and Muscle Metaphors teacher.

Nuala Bent BA; MSc; PhD.

Nuala has a background in Academic Research. Following a post Graduate degree in Research Methods, she worked for many years as Panel Manager of a longitudinal study researching into cognitive ageing at the University of Manchester and later as Senior Research Fellow (Rehab Medicine) at the University of Leeds.

Nuala was awarded her PhD in the Department of Epidemiology and Health Sciences, Faculty of Medicine, University of Manchester, in 1995.

Nuala has taken early retirement in order to pursue her career in Complimentary Therapies. Her passion is to raise awareness of the need for an integrated model of Healthcare.

She is a Plexus Bio Energy Therapist, Registered Reflexologist and Reiki Master.

Nuala is a member of the British Reflexology Association (BRA) and is currently registered with the Complimentary and Natural Healthcare Council (CNHC) for her Reflexology.

Nuala also holds a European Diploma in Bio-Energy Therapy.

Nuala has worked in the complimentary therapy field since 2003 and qualified as a Bio-Energy Therapist in 2010.

HIDDEN MIND
A JOURNEY OF RECONNECTION
Tom Griffin and Nuala Bent

Introduction

There are many reasons for writing this book, not least of which is to act as the interface between the reader and a greater understanding of the innate wisdom which we have at our disposal, in order to maintain a true balance of physical, emotional, mental and spiritual health. Although we have separate levels of these elements, they are all interconnected. People are becoming more aware of our interconnectedness albeit in an intangible way. For instance, we may have experienced flashes of insight from time to time which leave us with a sense of 'other knowledge' which at first encounter seems at odds with accepted norms. In such instances, we seem to be tapping into a reservoir of knowledge which although outside our everyday personal experiences, arouse in us a curiosity as to their source. The question is, how can we recall something we have never encountered or learned? Where does this reservoir of knowledge originate? How do we know we know? In order to find out we need to study our Universe in terms of how we resonate with it and to explore ancient esoteric knowledge and practices as to its source.

There is a new awakening of consciousness with regard to how we cope with the many diseases that are prevalent in our society and people are beginning to question the inevitability of the disease process. We now know more than ever about the human body. Never before have so many medications and treatments been available to so many people. This begs the question as to why so many diseases are on the increase in our western society. People are looking for answers and more of them are searching outside the current medical model and some have turned to natural medicine to find the answers. There is a need to look back into our past history in order to see how our ancestors coped with disease and to explore methods of healing used prior to the birth of the pharmaceutical industry.

The primary purpose of this book however, is to introduce the reader to the work of Tom Griffin within the concepts of the HiddenMind programme and to give it its true place in the history of our evolving consciousness. Consciousness is about coming to terms with our own personal power. It is about harnessing the power of our thoughts to influence our biology in a positive way. It is about knowledge.

It is also our intention to inform (educate) those readers who through a need for a solution for ongoing and unresolved health problems, happened upon it in a healing capacity, but who are mystified as to its source. It is a story of unfolding and reconnection to that mysterious arena of mind-body medicine.

Tom's programme involves Bio-energy, Vibrational Kinesiology and healing sounds and is the result of more than 30 years of study about how the body works, the development of diseases and the body's ability to heal itself.

Secondly, and closely related, is to reawaken for the reader the concept of the power-house we have within us in the form of the subconscious mind. We are powerful beyond our wildest dreams but for many people the path to their own personal power is not obviously accessible. This is due in part to the limitations and expectations of the current scientific paradigm, and partly to a belief system which ignores any kind of internal dialogue and self-healing, in favour of external academic and professional experience.

It has been suggested that we are each born with an inner knowledge of who we are and what our purpose is, but somehow along life's path, we become side-tracked by life and lose the memory. Tapping into the infinite knowledge of the Universe is our birth right, but we are hindered from being able to do so by our co-dependent nature. We suggest that the nature of our co-dependency is firmly rooted in our conditioning which in turn favours the dominant paradigm and the balance of power.

During the course of this book we will explore areas of consciousness from the revelations of new science and its relevance with respect to societal health and well-being.

In preparation for writing we have come across a treasure trove of Literature which engages different aspects of the subject, each in its own way contributing and supplying further pieces of the jigsaw that is the 'subconscious' mind. Over the past twenty years mind and body medicine has provided considerable evidence of the importance of the role of the mind in the treatment of illness. We can go back into the past to see how healing has worked for thousands of years, long before pharmaceutical companies came into being. For instance, in the shamanic tradition the concept of health involved four aspects: physical, mental, emotional and spiritual. This concept of health was based on people being in harmony with their surroundings. The separation came about in the western world in the 16th and 17th century with the redirection of science in order to demonstrate the control of humankind over nature. With the technological advancement of this era in terms of surgical equipment and techniques, the emotional and spiritual dimensions of the human body were no longer deemed relevant. Therefore, fixing and curing illness became a matter of science. We would suggest that there is a new consciousness of empowerment with regard to health and illness which has sparked a new enquiry as to the role of ancient knowledge, and the body's own capacity for healing.

Background to the Hidden Mind System

The HiddenMind Programme is a system founded and developed by Tom Griffin. It is a culmination of his twenty seven years working with bio-energy and bodywork, the Corrective Sound Programme and The Dawson Programme. Tom had the opportunity to study under the late Cameron Dawson ten years ago and became a Dawson Programme Practitioner. Tom also studied with Ellen Erikson in Denmark and qualified as a Corrective Sound Practitioner.

Similar to concepts of the Dawson programme, the HiddenMind programme is about the 'secrets' of human health based on a knowledge of the body's electrical systems, which include energy systems for basic body structure, the body's energy supply, the body's protection system and life energy. The Programme involves Bioenergy, Vibrational Kinesiology and the Investigative and Corrective Sound Protocol and is the result of more than 30 years of study about how the body works, the development of diseases and the body's ability to heal itself. It is a mix of Ancient wisdom and modern Western knowledge.

CHAPTER 1

The Metaphysics of Change

We live in exciting and changing times when fatalism is no longer the dogma of the day and humanity is undergoing transformation.

A new realization is dawning that we can be participators and not just passive observers in our changing world. Thanks to the advancement of science we now know that our universe is made up of vibrating energy that is constantly changing and expanding. In fact, we are vibrational beings in a vibrational universe that at its most fundamental level is composed of a combination of energy and consciousness[1]. From a metaphysical approach everything is seen as energy and all energy is perceived as interconnected. From this perspective, everything we call physical or real is energy and all energy is seen as the product of creative consciousness.

New science in the form of quantum physics tells us that we are interconnected with each other and our universe which suggests that we are each as individuals part of that awareness and as such are responsible for how it influences our world, both individually and collectively. In recognizing our interconnectedness, we can no longer behave as separate isolated individuals. There is a field of energy holding everything together and we are part of that field.

This metaphysical view of our interconnectedness is both empowering and challenging as it carries with it a responsibility for outcome. From this perspective there are no chance happenings as all our experiences, personal or otherwise, are the end result of our engagement with our consciousness which can be in harmony or disharmony with the universe depending on the nature of our thoughts.

As co-creators we ought to be able to reach our true potential in terms of health. This statement begs the question as to why so many people are seeking new solutions in terms of healing. Why have so many people succumbed to the ravages of the emerging diseases of our century? Can it be that the allopathic Newtonian model of medicine no longer serves our purpose? Modern medicine denies the value of intuition. It is an empiricism based on the assumption that x leads to y in a predictable format, ignoring the wider context. We are complex living systems and simple cause and effect pathways do not apply to complex systems[2]. New science is telling us that we create our own reality through our consciousness, but in terms of health, it is the body that is the receptor for that consciousness. If the body is not balanced then the consciousness of health and wellness cannot be expressed, in fact the fallout from the lack of balance often manifests as disease[3].

Can it be that we are so out of harmony with the universe and each other that we have a need to re-educate ourselves regarding our connection with the field of energy that is holding everything together?

There is nothing new in our universe, only rediscovery. Our consciousness is expanding daily and with it our thirst for knowledge about our universe and our connection with it. We are no longer prepared to sit back and let things unfold around us. Old knowledge that appeared lost is re-emerging. We are uncovering rather than discovering and our life's journey is one of reconnection. According to Barbara Wren in her book, "Cellular Awakening", we need to release old patterns of thinking regarding consciousness and not just accept what is fed to us almost on a daily basis through powerful institutions and channels. It would seem that there is an urgent need to understand phenomena at a much deeper level and to take our true place within the field of energy that is holding us in an energetic and vibrating embrace within the earth's energy[4].

We would suggest that there is a latent consciousness of healing within each of us that is part of the reconnection that is re-emerging with society's expanding consciousness and need for wholeness. It is part of the science of the energy field which in the words of Gregg Braden is "bridging the gap between science and spirituality". Indeed, it would seem that 'new science' is merely uncovering and reflecting to us what has been known for centuries within the world of mysticism and ancient religions[5].

HiddenMind – combining New Science and Ancient wisdom

One such example of ancient healing wisdom being accessed by people in need of healing is the 'HiddenMind' Investigative and corrective sound Protocol developed by Tom Griffin. He has now developed his own "Hiddenmind" protocol incorporating Bio Energy work, Vibrational Kinesiology, Muscle Testing and Dowsing, the Haraga Programme; Neuro Linguistic Programming and Bodywork Techniques learned from unique people around the world.

The hidden-mind protocol seeks to initiate the return of the body to its optimum condition through the correction of its electrical systems. It is based on more than 30 years of study about how the body works, the development of diseases and the body's ability to heal itself.

The 'hiddenmind' and corrective sound protocol involves the use of special sound frequencies as a method of correction. These sounds are used to communicate information to the conscious mind that has been blocked or locked into the sub-conscious due to trauma or shock, which can be physical, mental, emotional, toxic, hereditary or environmental. It recognises the supremacy of the sub-conscious mind in that it views the human body as a naturally self-creating, self-correcting system when given the opportunity to do so.

The hidden or subconscious mind knows the true essence of ourselves. It is the wisdom hidden deep within us, the inner voice, and the software which has logged our programming from conception until the present day. It is a repository of learned experiences which emits responses to environmental signals in line with the truths/ stimuli it has stored away. It is eminently more powerful than the conscious mind. The method is based on the premise that the body has a controlling and dynamic energy matrix around which the human body-form evolves through cell division[6] and was known to the ancient Egyptians, Chinese, Hindus, Buddhists and shamanic healers in Africa, Asia and South America. It is the basis of very old methods of healing such as, acupuncture, Tai Chi and yoga.

The human energy field makes up a part of the energetic matrix which is made up of seven auric fields, seven chakras and 14 meridians. These are the 28 cardinal frequencies that transmit information from the subconscious mind to the conscious brain. This energy, through its own intelligence, vibrates through to the very core of our being thereby unlocking the inner healing ability that lies dormant within every cell of our bodies.

Maintaining a healthy electro-physical system was common knowledge and practice in ancient times, the understanding of which has been resurfacing in the western culture more recently. For instance, Naturopaths and others working in the field of natural medicine would tell us that disease is lack of ease or harmony, or the result of a disorganised energy field. This is not based on fantasy but has been validated in laboratory type settings and will be discussed in more detail later in this book. We live in an electromagnetic environment and have a need to know how to influence the electromagnetic field of energy in order to restore the energy flow[7].

A brief introduction to Bio Energy

Everything in the world has its own energy frequency and, therefore, its own energy field which exists within the earth's energy field. Maintaining a healthy electro-physical system requires keeping our energy in a constant state of balance. A healthy system requires a vigilance as to what is going on at all levels, inside and outside the body. However, the pace of modern life is often a distraction and we can find ourselves distanced from how we truly should be. The human energy field can be manipulated and changed in such a way as to affect the health of an individual. The body is an energy system and the energy field is a blueprint of the physical body. By changing the vibration of your body, you can change its chemistry.

Most of our health problems have their origin in a destructive energy frequency, hence the necessity to find a modality within the arena of energy medicine which will help us to find the balance required to achieve optimum health.

Scientists, through Quantum Physics, have proven that energy healing works by the rewiring of the body on an energetic level. Encoded within specific electrical patterns, this energy field contains information which can be regarded as the original blueprint of the person being treated. All of this information very accurately reflects your current physical, emotional and mental state[8].

Thus, Bio-energy Therapy is a safe, non-invasive and highly effective form of energy medicine. It is termed "bio-energy" - the energy of life. Based on the body's natural ability to heal itself, bio-energy involves manipulating the energies within and outside the body to achieve balance. The imbalances are rectified either by drawing off energy to release a blockage or putting in energy to replenish a depletion.

Every cell is surrounded and supported by this energy which also acts like a transmitter and receiver, providing both a blueprint for the physical body and also acts as an information network between the body, mind and spirit. The basic principle underlying the therapy is that when we are healthy and life is good our system's energy flows freely and helps us to maintain health and well-being. Stress, illness, injury and emotional discord disrupt this flow.

Bio-energy, or life force energy, also emanates around the physical body in the form of bio-fields, creating a low frequency electromagnetic field, commonly known as an aura. In a larger context, bio-energy is an inseparable component of Energy. We are more than a simple biochemical mass. We are also an energetic being. Ancient healing traditions both acknowledge and treat using these principles.

Ancient civilisations were aware that the earth has its own magnetic lines and that it was possible to tap into the earth's energies (or more recently called life force energy). Science has begun to uncover through physics what was once considered the ravings of folklore and superstition. Scientific experiments discovered (or rather, uncovered) a rationale which verified the heretofore 'myths' and folklore of ancient civilisations and religions.

The fact that our bodies also have a magnetic field has implications for health based on the premise of quantum physics regarding the interconnectedness of everything in the universe. We are all connected with each other and through universal energy with the rest of the cosmos. Science is beginning to demonstrate that we are not "isolated beings living our desperate lives on a lonely planet in an indifferent universe"[9], but we were always at the centre of things, part of a whole. Each of us comes into this existence with a unique set of personal qualities. Our choices determine how we overcome the difficulties we encounter. Life has many possibilities and one of them is about choice. The universe is always in a state of balance. The possibility for the human body to be in balance is down to personal choice. The mind is like a magnet in that it attracts what it thinks most. Our thoughts and emotions play a part in the development of an illness, but they can also play a part in our healing. Living and healing are a journey. Let us make the right choices along the way. Every positive choice activates a new current of energy in our lives.

For instance, Caroline Myss tells us "Learn to sense the flow of energy inside and outside your body – all that is required is conscious attention"[10].

In the next few chapters we will explore the concept of energy and energy fields in terms of their relevance for optimal health and the capacity within each of us to activate our body's ability for self-healing. Once the energies have been balanced in a person's energy field, the conditions exist to allow them to heal their own illnesses.

CHAPTER 2

QUANTUM PHYSICS

The Cosmos Connection

The main purpose of this chapter is to remind ourselves and the reader of the power that is at our disposal in terms of health outcome and wellbeing. It is also to remind us that we all have an innate knowledge which has lost its impact. This is due to earlier conscious programing in line with Newtonian principles and a model of medicine based on outdated scientific principles, together with a paradigm which is inadequate for dealing with the diseases and welfare of our global community.

Science has moved on since Newton but as scientific truth is normally the remit of the scientific elites, most of us are unaware as to its impact on our lives. Scientific debate is not within the remit of our daily interaction as we have been programmed to think that it is not our concern. Consequently, desensitising from such programming demands a re-education in terms of trust and personal responsibility, both of which are based on knowledge and awareness. It is necessary to re-empower people and knowledge is power.

The basic premise behind any system of healing is to understand fully the human body and how it functions in relation to its own preservation, along with how it might interact with the cosmos. In order to understand the possibilities of empowerment with regard to perceptions of health and well-being it is necessary to examine changes in the scientific world of physics which lend support to a model of health based on personal responsibility.

In fact, science is now supporting what the mystics and ancient cultures have been telling us for centuries but because the message lacked scientific evidence, it was all dismissed as folklore or at worst, the outcome of delusions. Now science has moved on and with it our concept of our universe has changed dramatically as also has the concept of our connectedness with the cosmos.

There are amazing people out there who have had the expertise and courage to explore beyond the dominant scientific paradigm when required and to whom we owe a tremendous debt of gratitude for the knowledge they have contributed to the world of science and to ourselves as participators in that world. For instance, Dr Bjorn Nordenstrom who has established that the human body has an immense network of blood vessel 'cables' that are surrounded by electromagnetic fields. His success in reversing tumours by applying electrical currents based on a specific charge was ignored by the American Cancer Association but later the Chinese Government recognised the value of his work by honouring him in 2001 with a prestigious award. Because of his persistence in the face of adversity, and his vision, he has saved cancer patients all over the world.

In the past scientific evidence was based on false assumptions, in particular with regard to the theory that any part of the universe that doesn't have a physical component in evidence consists of empty space. Thanks to the investigation of modern day physics we now know that there is no empty space; rather there is a field of energy that pulls everything together and we are part of that field. The significance as to how this affects us will become clearer as we explore historically how modern day physics evolved.

In the classical physics world of Newton, everything in the universe was perceived as solid matter. However, even though science has moved on from the classical physics of Newton's era, it was an important era in science. His laws of motion and gravitation were an important advancement in providing a framework for dealing with large-scale things such as the movement of planets. By using Newton's laws engineers can work out when a spacecraft launched from earth is likely to reach Mars[2]. It was also the basis by which scientists were able to calculate orbits from satellites and was the scientific framework which enabled astronauts to land on the moon[3]. However, with the advancement of scientific enquiry it was evident that some things did not fit the dominant scientific paradigm and could no longer be explained by classical physics. In Newton's world of classical physics, the universe was seen as a machine and every-thing in it as its component parts.

A new paradigm was dawning which began with the discoveries of Albert Einstein, which changed the model of the universe from a material based to an energy based one. This discovery changed the beliefs of the scientific world dramatically. In his theory of relativity, Einstein showed that time and space are not as absolute as everyday experience would suggest. He proposed that time and space cannot be separated and he referred to his findings as the concept of space-time which he saw as a dynamic entity in which both exist together as a fourth dimension. This has led some scientists / researchers to conclude that Einstein believed that past and future are intimately entwined as the stuff of the fourth dimension, which is the meaning behind his theory of space-time. The idea of time as a fourth dimension is usually attributed to his theory of special relativity, in this sense, the fourth dimension concerns how two kinds of perception work together as we interact with objects or people in space. It is making assumptions based on prior knowledge, without having to verify that knowledge in a specific situation. An interesting and possibly non-scientific interpretation is that the concept relates to the act of perceiving (consciousness) or feeling (sensation)[4]. Another legacy of relativity theory is the formula $E=mc^2$ which states that energy and mass are in fact, equivalent.

According to Newtonian physics, it was believed that atoms and their constituents consisted of a solid mass or a solid physical object. It was not until some years later that Einstein's research showed that atoms could be broken down and that the subatomic particles which collectively formed the atoms, are composed of pure energy. This discovery brought a new understanding of the universe and with it, a need to develop a new branch of physics which could deal with discrete indivisible units of energy, such as the subatomic particles of Einstein's physics. Thus a new science of quantum physics was developed in the 20th Century in order to address discoveries which couldn't be explained by Newton's Laws. It was therefore, born out of classical physics as a scientific platform from which to explain the behaviour of matter and energy at microscopic levels. It forms the basis of elementary particle physics and has been hugely successful at explaining the behaviour of things that are smaller than the atom.

The shift came about with the discovery that the subatomic particles which collectively formed the atoms, are composed of pure energy. According to the principles of quantum physics, all matter is made up of energy and there are no absolutes. In the quantum world, matter only exists as a possibility and the entire universe is actually a series of probabilities. This theory was the brain child of Max Planck who developed the theory alongside other scientists.

At the quantum level, everything that exists in the universe is vibrating and oscillating at different rates. Einstein believed that the energy he had discovered was in the form of particles and therefore had an appearance of being solid. However this theory differed from that of physicist Thomas Young, who stated that energy existed as a wave form and not as particles at all[5].

This theory of energy existing as particles was taken a step further in 1922 by findings of scientist and Nobel Prize winner Niels Bohr, who hypothesised that energy could be both waves and particles. Waves are encoders and carriers of information, however, in the quantum world both a wave view and a particle view are necessary to describe fully the nature of light as well as matter at the smallest scale.

This dual model in physics known as the principle of complementarity means that the subatomic particles existed as both particles and wave forms but that they were mutually exclusive in that they couldn't appear as both at the same time. Rather, it was the thoughts and perception of the scientist doing the observing that determined which one it would be. In other words, the observation of the scientist converted wave forms into particles of matter. The energy once observed acts in accordance with the way it is believed it will act and will provide a physical appearance based on the perception of the thinker. Experiments in quantum physics show that by just focusing our awareness on something as miniscule as an electron and by focusing attention on what it is doing, changes its properties while we are watching it. What quantum physics has shown is that everything is energy including ourselves, and as such we are in tune with our universe. Everything begins as a wave in the quantum field and is transformed into the physical realm in accordance with the beliefs of the observer.

This discovery has far reaching implications for us in terms of health and wellbeing. For instance, there are many significant changes in our planet reported, all of which are significant in terms of health outlook. The first is that earth's speed of vibration and its resonance is thought to be increasing, while the earth's magnetic field is getting considerably weaker. Based on past experiences this could result in a reversal of the magnetic poles, which would have implications for anything influenced magnetically. As iron is influenced magnetically and we have high concentrations of iron levels in our body's blood supply, it is not rocket science to suggest that this would effect a change in the human body. For instance, a reduction in magnetic strength gives us the potential to think more expansively and more freely[6].

Another change thought to influence us concerns the fact that everything in the universe vibrates with energy. This vibration, known as the Schumann Resonance, has been steadily increasing over a number of years. Wren says that the connection with regards to the health of mankind is that some of the glands in the human body tune into this vibration; the hypothalamus and the pituitary glands. Our cells have receptors in the protein channels that pick up all vibrations from outside making us more connected to changes in vibration. Wren suggests that we have the potential to increase our own vibrations, thereby increasing our awareness and connections, and consequently, gaining access to our inner wisdom.

There has also been a huge change in photon activity, which has resulted in an increase in light both in our solar system and on our planet. In the past, such increases in photon activity were commensurate with advances in thinking and development[7].

So far we have looked at changes in magnetic capacity and the availability of light and the possible implications for health. But, we know that the universe itself constitutes a mass of electro-magnetic light waves in gravitational movement, and that these waves are continually in a state of motion or vibration. Also every molecule and every atom of this universe is in constant vibration. Living cells are self-charging condensers built on the fundamental plan of the atom. Every human body cell is composed of atoms and has a nucleus of solar electricity which dominates its magnetic force. The energy in our cells is influenced by our thoughts and mental vibrations. This will be discussed in greater detail in a later chapter. Energy and vibration are synonymous. Every life cell in man vibrates and has its own frequency and wave-length. All life is energy and all energy is vibration and vibration in turn is energy[8].

At the quantum level everything that exists in the Universe is vibrating and oscillating at different rates. One theory is that energy exists on a continuum from the densest (physical matter) to the least dense (spiritual energy). Another theory is that 2 previously connected quantum particles separated by vast distances remain somehow connected. If one particle is changed the other changes instantaneously, so at the quantum level all energy is connected. We are continually in contact with cosmic forces and these energies are extremely powerful. We have to concede that energy vibration and cosmic energy vibration has a profound effect on our lives and that we are all connected and in tune with the universe through the medium of energy.

How does this manifest? We are not victims of circumstances and can effect a change in our life circumstance based on a change in beliefs and thoughts and emotions. We have the ability to mould and shape the various areas of our lives in accordance with how we think, believe and feel. It would seem that a new reality is dawning that every-thing in our world is connected to everything else.

Braden suggests that in order for the imaginary ideas of one moment in time to become the reality of another, there must be something that links them together; a field of energy that connects everything.

CHAPTER 3

The Human Biofield

The Biofield is a scientific term for the multi-layered protective field that surrounds and penetrates the human body. It is often referred to as the aura but a more accurate description from the hidden mind perspective is the auric fields. This shield or field of energy emanates from the body and interacts with the energies of our environment. It acts as a protective shell around the body and expands or contracts in accordance with how well it resonates with the energy of the immediate environment. This field of energy is thought to be as important to our wellbeing as the oxygen we breathe.

Understanding the Anatomy and Physiology of the human biofield is of huge importance for health as it is thought that it may carry novel information of diagnostic value for medicine[1]. With the re-emergence of energy based complementary healing modalities, a new interest has evolved which extends beyond the level of understanding required by energy therapists, but embraces more scientific exploration into the energy fields of the human body. In a few decades scientists have gone from a conviction that there is no such thing as an energy field to not only acknowledging that it exists but to exploring its role in health and disease.

For example, as far back as 1998 the Centre for Biofield Sciences (CBS) was established at the Maharastra Instsiute of Technology's World Peace Centre as a fully equipped research laboratory in order to map the human biofield and explore its significance in modern healthcare. In 2004, the human biofield was recognised by the National Institutes of Health (USA) and can now be referenced in a number of research papers accessible through PubMed. This is due in part to the upsurge of interest in healing modalities and to the availability of sensitive instruments such as the SQUID (superconducting quantum interference device) designed by scientists to detect the minute energy vibrations around the body[2].

However, to date, most of the information concerning the biofield has not come from scientific discovery, but rather from the vast resource of esoteric knowledge of ancient spiritual and medical traditions. Indigenous systems of healing going back thousands of years are based on concepts of a life force. For instance, the Ayurvedic system is based on a life force energy called Prana; in Chinese medicine it is known as Qi. It is thought that the vital life force energy of Prana or Qi, is what we now refer to as the present-day concept of the biofield. Further similarities would appear to exist between these ancient concepts of the life force and modern concepts of a biofield, in the assumption that a form of life-giving energy flows throughout the body and that illness arises as a result of blockages, excesses, or irregularities in its flow.

It has been established that the human body and the energy field that surrounds it are made up of electromagnetic energy. The discovery that the electromagnetic output of different parts of the body are detectable by scientific instruments has been used in mainstream medicine for some time. For example, a theory about the existence of brain waves by Austrian Psychiatrist Hans Berger[3] resulted in his inventing a machine that proved his theory. Namely, the Electroencephalograph or EEG. As a result of his theories it is now commonly accepted that there are six brain wave states; the four main ones being, beta, alpha, theta, and delta. However, the existence of gamma and lambda waves are still somewhat contentious. The discovery of the EEG was followed closely by the discovery by Nobel Prize winner, Einthoven, a Dutch doctor and physiologist, that the electrical frequencies of the heart could be measured by another scientific instrument (ECG). Both of these discoveries have demonstrated that the brain and the heart both contain an electrical field which can be measured.

Although the interest in relationships in biochemistry has been expanding over recent years, which culminated in the Human Genome Project, only a small number of scientists around the world have worked to understand the energy fields of the human body. It has been general knowledge for some time that activities of cells and tissue generate electrical fields that can be detected on the skin surface. However, as it was considered that these fields were too tiny to detect, biologists assumed they could have no physiological significance. This began to change when scientists discovered the electro-magnetic field projected from the human heart. This was a doughnut shaped field of energy that surrounds the heart and extends beyond the body. This was the discovery of scientists at the Institute of HeartMath, who carried out experiments to explore the power of human emotion on the body[4]. Experiments carried out on the effects of emotion on DNA produced significant and life changing results: human emotion changed the shape of human DNA. Different intention produced different effects on the DNA molecule.

Subsequently it has been discovered that all tissues and organs produce specific magnetic pulsations, or bio-magnetic fields, which have complemented the traditional electrical recordings.

It is a known fact that the human body emits low-level light, heat and has electrical and magnetic properties based on the electromagnetic field theory of modern physics. However, no agreement has been reached in the scientific community on the definition of the biofield and western medicine continues to focus on the physiology and chemistry of the body. Hence, measuring the biofield and understanding its role continues to have inherent problems for scientists both because of the intangible nature of the field and the scarcity of funding for such projects.

Results from preliminary and pilot studies have described the biofield as "a flickering flame of energy: dynamic, with some coherence and stability and with some elements of chaos and unpredictability" Beverly Rubik, writing in the Journal of Alternative and Complementary Medicine, provides a scientific foundation for its existence. She argues that the important difference between traditional and modern views of the vital life force is that the biofield rests on physical principles and can be measured, whereas traditional concepts remain metaphysical[5].

One possible influence of biofield phenomena, according to Rubik, is that they may act directly on molecular structures, changing the conformation of molecules in functionally significant ways. She goes a step further in suggesting an influence in the transfer of bio information carried by very small energy signals interacting directly with the energy fields of life. The work of cell biologist Bruce Lipton supports this view in that he had observed that diseased tissue emits its own unique energy signature which is different to that emitted by surrounding health cells[6].

So far our discussion about the acceptance of the existence of a biofield has rested on the measurement of different parts of the body via scientific instruments. However other scientists have demonstrated that the electromagnetic output of the whole body can be measured. When measuring the output of energy from the chakras, Dr Valerie Hunt found that most people in the sample measured within the normal range but when tests were carried out on people who used healing energies, it was found that their frequencies registered in a much higher band[7].

The idea of a universal life energy is the guiding principle of many current forms of healing. For instance, Bio energy practitioners are trained to assess imbalances in the human biofield either with their hands or intuitively. Similar practices using the same principles of scanning and intuition are Reiki, a form of Japanese spiritual healing and Qigong Therapy. However, these modalities propose a challenge to the dominant medical paradigm because they cannot be explained by the usual biochemical mechanisms.

Rubik[8] goes on to suggest that there are other mysteries in biology and medicine that appear to involve interacting energetic fields. She mentions the mystery of regenerative healing in animals, and the mystery of embryonic development of the fertilized egg to an organized integral animal, which may also involve innate energy fields. She concedes that based on the dual model of complementarity in quantum theory, an 'energy field' view of life may need to be seen as complementary rather than antagonistic to the bio molecular view, in order to provide us with some answers to the as yet unsolved mysteries of life.

However, this brings us to the cutting edge of biofield research – the question as to how the biofield may shift as a result of a shift in consciousness. As far back as the 1920's and 30's research was validating the existence of a bio-magnetic field now commonly known as an energy/ bio field, and provided evidence that pathology alters the bio-magnetic field. In other words, disease could be detected by changes in the energy field before the physical symptoms presented[9].

More recent studies have validated this hypothesis and research by Dr Valerie Hunt of U.C.L.A, has supported earlier findings that disease begins at an energetic level. Hunt observed that before the brain was activated, before stimuli altered the heart rate, blood pressure or breathing, the energy field had already responded. This led her to postulate that a person's primary responses in their world, first takes place in the energetic or auric field, and not in the sensory nerves or in the brain as believed by mainstream medicine.

Dr Hunt reports that the energetic emanations of the body show disintegrating changes before actual disease conditions can be diagnosed. Others also found that the magnetic energy increased at the site of an injury, flowing from the centre of the body outwards[10]. This agrees with Hunt's findings that the magnetic flow precedes changes in attending current activity. For instance, she found that an increase in magnetic energy preceded a change in consciousness. The same held for changes in emotions or any dramatic change in the electrical energy. Her data also shows the first "chaos" patterns ever demonstrated in biological systems. In mapping the bioenergy fields, Dr Hunt has found that each individual has a unique vibrational energy pattern, in the same way that we have unique fingerprints from our DNA. She calls this the Signature Field. The Signature Field of a healthy human being is composed of balanced, coherent energy patterns across the full spectrum of frequencies. This coherency shows up on a graph as smooth, gentle, shallow waves evenly distributed throughout the frequency spectrum.

Whereas, the Signature Fields of human beings who have (or are soon going to develop) disease show two kinds of patterns: deficiency patterns, and hyperactive patterns. These show up on the graph as thick, jagged waves concentrated in the high- or low-frequency bands. Deficiency diseases like cancer and fatigue syndrome have anti-coherent patterns in the high frequency ranges, with almost no energy at all in the lower frequencies. Hyperactive conditions like colitis, hypertension, and skin problems show anti-coherent patterns in the low frequencies, with absent vibrations on the high frequencies. So basically, when people are seriously ill we they have lost their natural rhythm and coherence.

But physiological symptoms appear because of the field disturbance. If we correct the disturbance in the field, the symptoms begin to disappear and the body begins to initiate healing. If we treat the symptoms directly, then when a stressful situation once more aggravates the incoherent energy that is the source of the problem, the disease condition returns.

Dr Hunt has discovered in her Aura-Meter laboratory that healing is an active process. We do not passively "react to" a healing modality. Rather, we "transact with" it. Her work scientifically proves the existence of the human energy field and the importance of a rich electromagnetic field for optimum health. She suggests that concepts of energy field transaction introduces a new perspective on illness and healing. Quantum coherence means that subatomic particles are able to co-operate. From this perspective these waves know about each other and are interlinked by bands of electromagnetic fields thus supporting a holographic effect.

It seems that we can describe the human biofield as an energetic matrix that surrounds the human body which directly links the cellular activity with the meridian pathways. Referring to the elusivity of the bio field, John Muir (1911) wrote," if we try to pick out anything by itself, we find it hitched to everything else in the universe"[11].

While this statement goes beyond Einstein's theory of relativity, that physical reality is not fixed and that there is an interdependency with everything, it also highlights the limitations of the theory. Einstein believed that we are passive observers living in a universe that is already in place over which we have very little influence.

It would seem that a new paradigm is dawning in which we are participators. Modern science would seem to support the view that the biofield is an intelligent energy system in constant communication with the human body and its immediate environment. Even pain occurs in the field before it is felt in the body. Modern physics concept of a field is that it is a continuous medium of transmission and info storage.

All vibrations are organised into fields which have their own integrity and which have the capacity to react, interact and unite with all other fields, which has led to the conclusion that the internal dynamics of the human biofield are based on its emotional organisation. Hunt's work displays a continuum of frequencies ranging from low energy frequencies at the level of the body's biological processes to high level frequencies associated with the mind-field and awareness. Hunt states that every emotion temporarily restructures the field. Activated emotions can increase the electromagnetic flow of the field, but emotions can also arise from an altered electromagnetic environment. For instance, in a situation where the electromagnetic flow of the energy field is interrupted, the body slides into a chaotic reaction precipitating illness and then, by readjusting, heals itself [12]. Jan deVries tells us that emotion means that energy is moving out, and disease is the result of disorganised electrical forces. Hence the importance of understanding the human body and how to influence the electromagnetic field of energy, in order to be in good health [13].

We suggest that such concepts of field energy transactions introduces a new perspective on illness and healing and are closely allied with the precepts of Bio-energy healing concerning the concept of blockages in the energy flow that result in disease. Jan deVries suggest that the human body is a microcosm in a macrocosm and is subject to all the physical, chemical and electrical laws that govern the universe. The body has three magnetic fields and as such is an extension of the earth. Our energy systems are in constant vibration and are connected with all the energy of the universe.

Systematic research has been conducted in support of the view that everything is connected to the energy matrix, the underlying field of energy that connects everything in creation. It is the bridge that connects past to present in terms of health and wellbeing. It unfolds for us the connections of ancient wisdom that have long since been forgotten and which have a great significance for the future of our planet and for the wellbeing of mankind.

This has positive implications for recent developments in the area of mind-body medicine.

CHAPTER 4

The New Science of Epigenetics

New scientific thinking is having far reaching effects way beyond the confines of how we view our world and is changing the way we think about our role with regard to genetic legacy. We would appear to be moving into a different reality with regard to our involvement and are surely on the edge of a paradigm shift as regards our concepts of personal power and control over the hereditary process. Part of that new shift in scientific thinking brought us to a new understanding as regards our part in the whole process. This is down to a shift away from the central dogma of orthodox biology in which DNA is the primary hereditary molecule, towards the new science of the genome. From the former perspective we are merely vehicles for the transfer of genetic material[1] but from the perspective of the new science we have the wherewithal within our own consciousness to assume a new role as participators.

It seems that while biological sciences are still stuck in the old paradigm based on Newtonian physics, new discoveries in physics itself is changing our world view. We refer to the relatively new science of Epigenetics. This is a revolutionary field in biology which changes our understanding about how life is controlled. It is described in the biological sciences literature as a study of a change in organisms caused by modification of gene expression through cell division without involving any changes in the DNA sequence. In fact, it is the study of mechanisms that turn the genes on and off. It is a fairly new scientific field which has grown in recent years and has transformed the way we think about genomes[2].

Prior to the new science of epigenetics, the dominant paradigm was based on Newtonian principles in that it perceives the body as a machine. From this perspective one is a victim of one's life circumstance and, in the case of diseases, of genetic determinism. Inherent in this prevailing paradigm is the belief that the blueprint for building and maintaining the body is the sole responsibility of our genes. Historically this was based on wrong assumptions that genes control life and that DNA alone was responsible for patterns of health. Exposure to illness was thought to be the direct result of inherited genes passed on from parent to child but leading edge science does not support this unilateral approach.

Thanks to the ground breaking research by Dr Bruce Lipton, which challenges the view that genetic design is predetermined by inherited chromosomes, there is scientific evidence that there is a genetic code that controls the gene but it is not DNA. Instead there are specific patterns of electromagnetic radiation which regulate DNA, RNA and protein synthesis, alter protein shape and function, and control gene regulation together with many other fundamental processes. While the genetic code is the same in every cell, the epigenetic code is tissue- and cell-specific. It can however, be influenced by several factors including age, the environment, and disease state.

Research by Dr Lipton[3] has proven that DNA is controlled from signals outside the cell, including the energetic messages emanating from our negative and positive thoughts. However, this is not new information. Hundreds of scientific studies over a number of years have revealed that every facet of biological regulation is profoundly impacted by the invisible forces of the electromagnetic spectrum.[4] Such important and paradigm changing information was available to scientists for some time, but ignored by mainstream biologists until the work of Dr Lipton who has shown scientifically within his laboratory that our thoughts, behaviours and mind-set all have a profound effect on our personal lives and consequently on our biology. This is an important message, given that our thoughts are influenced by our perception of the environment as well as from conditioning beliefs stored in the subconscious mind from childhood.

Perceptions are based on beliefs, which influence how we think and behave and all of which influence the body to respond in accordance with the messages we are sending to it. The body is amazing in that it is designed to adjust itself to respond to the environment, but the response is generated by the mind which interprets the environment. How you see the world causes your body to make a response to keep it alive. If the mind interprets the environment correctly, then the biology conducts the appropriate physiology and metabolism to enable the body to stay alive. But, if we have a misperception then the cells respond to the wrong information and control our biology accordingly. The cells can't see the environment. They only respond to what we sense. For instance, the sensation of cold or heat is a perception, which in turn is a signal to the body to adjust the metabolism accordingly. The perception of cold causes the body to activate the switch to turn up the temperature and warm the body, whereas the perception of heat will cause a change in the internal biology which causes the body to sweat in order to drop the temperature so that it doesn't overheat.

The importance of having perceptions that are accurate and not part of earlier self-sabotaging beliefs that were downloaded into our subconscious when we were children, can be seen in the body's response to fear. If we have a perception that there is something to be afraid of, then the body chemistry informs the cells to shut down the growth processes, and consequently puts us into a protection response. If we stay in fear, then the chemistry of our body stays in protection mode and also shuts down the immune system. This leaves us susceptible to attacks from within the body to which we would not normally be susceptible and which would be dealt with by a fully operating immune system, as is the norm when the body is not in fear mode.

The more fear you are in the more you are diminishing the power of your entire biology and you are no longer sustaining life. The body responds physiologically to protect itself by releasing chemicals appropriate to the situation. A cell can be in a growth or protection response, but it cannot be in both at the same time. They are both mutually exclusive with the growth response moving towards enhancing growth and the protection response moving away from the threat[5]. It is the nervous system that monitors and interprets the environmental signals and consequently organises appropriate responses.

One response that we are all familiar with is the fight or flight response. In this case the cells respond to something the nervous system perceives as a threat. The cells go into a protection response sending appropriate chemicals into the body to deal with the intrusion. This response, known in biology as the HPA axis, involves the hypothalamus, the pituitary and adrenal glands. The HPA axis is inactive when there is no threat. When activated, the adrenal hormones stop the immune system from working to conserve energy. In addition, the adrenal stress hormones constrict the hormones in the forebrain reducing its ability to function, thereby interfering with our ability to think clearly. It also represses activity in the brain's prefrontal cortex, diminishing our conscious awareness.

If we live in fear the body chemistry shuts down the growth process, and the immune system. In fact, it is winding down the life functions in order to enhance survival. However, this protection response was never intended to be a continuous solution, but only meant as a mechanism to relieve situations of acute stress. If we continue to be in fear, then the HPA axis response will be activated unnecessarily with some cost to our health. There is also the cost to the body of the effects of flooding it with adrenal stress hormones indefinitely, leaving the body in a continual state of heightened sensitivity awaiting a non-event with the additional complication of diminished conscious awareness and reduced intelligence[6].

For instance, it is not good for the body to be saturated with adrenaline as the body would eventually become fatigued waiting for an event that is never going to start. Hence the need for the body not to be misinformed by fear-based perceptions which are untrue.

You might well ask how this is relevant for healing. Bruce Lipton tells us that we have the capacity for healing within our own bodies in the form of stem cells. These cells are scattered throughout the body and are the equivalent of embryonic cells. Their main function is to replace, repair and maintain the body. The presence of such cells would indicate a case in point that the body has the capacity to self-heal and the findings of Dr Lipton's work supports that viewpoint.

However, if you have a perception that you can't heal yourself then that is what the cells will respond to and the body's capacity to self-heal will be compromised. While you continue in this perception, you will negate the ability of your own stem cells to repair your body. However, the new approach to biology tells us that if we change our self-limiting pre-programmed beliefs that we are victims and have no control over our health, we can change our perceptions and thereby enhance and engage the stem cells that are present in our body since birth. Then we are participators in our own healing.

This is a new understanding of the nature of the part that genes have to play in protecting the body and maintaining it in a state of homeostasis. Genes instruct cells to produce proteins or other molecules. Each cell undergoes a vast number of chemical reactions, one of which is methylation. It is this process, together with proteins called histones, which work together to guide the cell into knowing which type of cell it is to become e.g. a kidney rather than a liver cell. However, as all the chromosomes and genes in the nucleus of every cell are identical, it is a mystery as to how the cells know where they need to go. Donna Eden suggests that in the absence of enlightenment from western science with regard to this mystery, we may need to consider an energy field, where the information is more or less broadcast to the genes[7].

Bruce Lipton tells us that conventional medicine views the body like a machine, and when the machine breaks down, we blame the machine. On this premise, all health problems and diseases are determined by the machine and we are all victims of our inherited genes. Dr Lipton's work has given us scientific evidence that this is not the case. The new model states that while genes are involved in the making of the machine, 95% of us have an adequate genome to have a healthy existence. The new model tells us that we are the drivers of the machine and as such we need to pay attention to the manner of our driving. In terms of health and wellbeing, our manner of 'driving' is related to how we see the world. We actually control our genes with our thoughts, beliefs and behaviours and this in turn influences our biology. Our thoughts are converted into signals sent to the cells and the information received by the cells is converted into bio-chemistry. The cells change their biology according to the chemicals produced from the nature of our thoughts and perceptions. This is the body's response to keep it alive in the world[8].

There is a need to explore the link between mind and matter with regard to perceptions of health and well-being. It appears that we are moving towards a new paradigm of owner responsibility for health outcome. Not only does this challenge our perceptions of who we are, but it puts us firmly into the position of playing an integral part in the interconnectedness of the quantum universe. We are no longer passive observers, but players in the field of quantum possibilities.

The role of perception and mind is now becoming the focal point in allopathic healthcare as they try to unravel the mysteries of the placebo effect and the role of psychosomatic stress[9]. It would seem that the new science of epigenetics is changing our world. The realisation that we can change our biology by retraining our thinking is a powerful message. It may well be the missing link between life and consciousness[10].

CHAPTER 5

New Consciousness

As we have already noted, we live in changing times whereby the whole of humanity and our planet would seem to be undergoing a transformation. There is a new awareness that our personal experiences within the framework of our personal small worlds are not happening by chance. We are waking up to realising our own potential and to an understanding that the patterns that exist in our lives are a reflection of our own consciousness. For instance, one scientist has suggested that living is a transaction, an interaction with other force fields with an element of choice[1]. The underlying machinery of consciousness doesn't change but keeps following the same principles. These appear to be in the main about awareness, harmony and balance. The simplest definition of consciousness according to Deepak Chopra is awareness. He states that the two are synonymous. Pure consciousness, because it underlies everything, is pure potential[2].

New science and new biology are supporting this view. The ultimate stuff of the universe is consciousness. Others talk about the 'wave nature' of consciousness, postulating that it is only at the interface between consciousness and the environment that constitutes reality. Dr Valerie Hunt suggests that ultimate reality is not contacted through the physical sense of the material world but through deep intuition. For instance, she suggests that as living systems transact with their attractors, they build a complex repertoire of vibrations which results in a memory. However, different people display different patterns of vibrations. Some can transact with an open field while others have exhausted the possibilities within a narrow width because if the human field does not transact, it loses its complexity and consequently has a diminished capacity for creative exploration. However, the idea of matter arising out of consciousness can seem quite foreign to our western minds because we have no experience of altering matter by will[3].

However, consciousness remains an emotive issue and there is more than one school of thought regarding the scientific basis that such a state exists. For instance, classical scientists deny the existence of consciousness, having no means of measuring it in terms of scientific theory.

Another body of thought based on materialist and neurobiological models maintains that consciousness is a manifestation of the brain and the neurons. Our brains are currently seen as machines that have parts called neurons which are said to be responsible for creating our thoughts. Earlier investigations based on the neural correlates of consciousness have proposed that brain systems become active in tandem with the conscious experience. More recent work focused on specific areas of the brain such as those areas affected by anaesthesia and also areas of decreased brain activity associated with vegetative states.

John Grandy[4], reporting on the above work, argues that each region of the brain is composed of specialised neurons which are unique to that region and he concludes that the proper functioning of neurons is pivotal to the process of human consciousness as well. However, his own investigation defines consciousness as the "interaction of things", such as, an organism, a DNA molecule or an atom, with other things such as, the external environment, different forms of energy and forces. This form of scientific investigation has become known as' the Interaction-based theory' of consciousness.

In his work, Grandy demonstrates a link between DNA and human consciousness. By this premise, everything in the universe ranging from quarks, to molecules, to brains to cells has some degree of consciousness. He argues that the importance of DNA consciousness lies in the ability of the DNA molecule to create and store genetic information. Based on his research, Grandy argues that DNA appears to function not only as a protein builder (the minority function) but also as a medium for the storage, receiving, and communicating of information.

The knowledge that human DNA can be influenced and modulated by frequencies (sound, light, language, and thought) has been known to mystics and teachers, over the ages. It may well be that the generational handing down of thought-focused exercises such as prayer, music and chanting is in some way related to this knowledge. For instance, an example of how the myths of ancient cultures hold knowledge outside of the experience of their own timeframe is verified in the work of Jeremy Narby[5], an anthropologist and writer who spent several years living with the Ashaninca people in the Peruvian amazon. During this time he sponsored an expedition for biologists to go to the rainforest to study indigenous knowledge systems.

In his book, The Cosmic Serpent, Narby takes a serious look at how neurogenetic consciousness informs awareness, knowledge, symbolism and culture. He reports on how Shamans, with the use of sophisticated neurotransmitter potions to induce visions, take their consciousness down to the molecular level and gain access to information related to DNA, which they call "animate essences" or "spirits."

Narby began his work of exploration with the Peruvian Indians, who claim that their knowledge of chemical interactions has its origins in plant-induced (ayahusca) type hallucinations. He observed that during these hallucinatory experiences these indigenous peoples acquired information that could not be accessed by any other methods. In their visions they report seeing double helixes, twisted ladders and chromosome shapes. Narby suggests that this is how shamanic cultures have known for millennia that the vital principle is the same for all living beings, and is shaped like two entwined serpents. They have even drawn the double helix structure, something which was only discovered by conventional science as late as 1953. Although this knowledge was acquired during non-rational states of consciousness, Narby argues that the Shamans metaphoric explanations correspond accurately with the descriptions that biologists are starting to provide, and that such knowledge is empirically verifiable.

The current scientific paradigm postulates that our thoughts are merely side effects of the working of our neurons[6]. The problem with this paradigm is that it does not convey the full picture of reality. From a dominant model perspective, there is no consensus as to what part of the brain, if any, may be responsible for consciousness. "When we operate within a mechanistic paradigm all we can do is track mechanistic changes such as chemical changes in neurons that occur when memories are created"[7]. Laughton goes on to argue that we are not going find out anything with such methods because the methods themselves are designed to examine the effects of consciousness and not the cause.

However, as discussed in earlier chapters, physics is changing and the effects are trickling into the rest of science. This continues to be problematic for investigation into the role of consciousness within the field of biological sciences, and indeed for medicine as well, as both areas remain within the dominant paradigm of health which does not take quantum theory into account.

The idea of a collective or world consciousness has been floating around for some time. The work of Garjajev and his Russian colleagues on hyper-communication would seem to suggest that a form of inter-dimensional communication may exist which has a parallel within nature. For instance, take the example of a colony of ants; when the queen ant is separated from her colony, the worker ants continue to build and construct the colony as if following some form of plan. However, if the queen ant is killed, all the work in the colony ceases, suggesting that the plan can no longer be accessed and group consciousness ceases to operate[8].

Further support for the role of group consciousness operating within nature can be seen in the life cycle of the monarch butterfly[9]. Monarch butterflies go through four stages during one life cycle, and through four generations in one year. The monarch was the first butterfly to have its genome sequenced. Recent research has identified the specific areas in the genome of the monarch that regulate migration. There appears to be no genetic difference between a migrating and non-migrating monarch but the gene is expressed in migrating monarchs but not expressed in non-migrating monarchs. The four generations are actually four different butterflies going through these four stages during one year until it is time to start over again with stage one and generation one.

The fourth generation is born in September and October and goes through exactly the same process as the first, second and third generations. However, the fourth generation of monarch butterflies does not die after two to six weeks. Instead, this generation migrates to warmer climates like Mexico and California and will live for six to eight months until it is time to start the whole process over again. It is amazing how the four generations of monarch butterflies works out so that the monarch population can continue to live on throughout the years, but not become overpopulated. The intuitive consciousness of Mother Nature!

We might ask how this relates to the quantum physics model. Physicist Amit Goswami, speaking about the nature of particles and how they respond to our observations, suggests that in order for an experiment to be observed, a conscious entity must be present, such as someone witnessing it. In fact he goes a step further in proposing that consciousness may be fundamental to reality. This means that matter emerges from consciousness and not the other way round[10].

This poses a paradoxical situation for neuroscientists who are conducting experiments to prove that consciousness arises out of the activity of the neurons. Consciousness lies deep in everything that is part of our universe. Every atom, molecule and living cell all arise from an underlying sea of consciousness. The fact that the brain is also made up of atoms rescinds the paradox, as it means that the brain itself also consists of consciousness. From this perspective, modern science is reminding us what mystics and ancient traditions have been telling us for centuries. However we have to be aware that there are still many scientists who are closed to such a viewpoint.

Fortunately there are more open-minded people in science who are willing to investigate consciousness, eg. Edgar Mitchel and other such eminent people who are willing to accept the deeper implications of quantum physics, but we will return to this in a later chapter. This brings us to the concept of the Universe as a hologram – a sea of information, with the part reflecting the whole. What we have is a universal intelligence. Laughton describes this storage site for universal intelligence as a quantum vacuum or a Zero Point Field. Based on this view, we can conclude that consciousness is everywhere and our brains are simply the conduit for it. Each of us relates to the quantum vacuum in a unique way. We can bring information into our lives that is unique to us. By tapping deeper into the field we are actually tuning into our own consciousness at a deeper level.

Research into collective consciousness carried out by Radin D and Nelson R, with the use of a REG machine, produced amazing results. It was the first inkling that group consciousness working through a medium such as the Zero Point Field acted as the universal organising factor in the cosmos[11]. These findings may have implications for the explanation of such phenonema as remote healing, remote sensing, and telepathy.

The new discoveries in neuroscience, quantum biology, and quantum physics have shown that a form of nonlocal connected consciousness has a physical-scientific foundation. What this means in terms of influence is that our thoughts and awareness are not confined to the small personal world we inhabit but can travel over vast distances as a type of telepathy. However, there is much debate and dissension dissention regarding the study of such phenomena, even when rigorous scientific research methods were used. Laughton sums it up beautifully in her book, Punk Science, when she suggests that skepticism may be an example of the very paradigm which its members wish to disprove; that the universe differs according to your perspective[12]. Thus it may be that non-local effects are outside their reality, and therefore, there is no observation.

Once again we are reminded that we are living in a vibrational universe comprised of both energy and consciousness with which we have a connection. As human beings, we are active players in the field in constant transaction with the universe. What this demonstrates is that certain spiritual or transcendental states of collective oneness have a valid basis within the new scientific paradigm and the possibility that they will be explained within the framework of quantum mechanics.

We must learn to accept that our thinking is a great and tangible spiritual force for change. This is something most people need to relearn as we are programmed in a culture of dependence on outside forces. Consequently, we need to expand our consciousness, releasing old ideas that hold us back from further enquiry and the need to understand phenomena at deeper levels, and not just accept what we are told[13].

Consciousness is an activity of the entire universe. Everything is conscious. If we accept that, we are part of a living whole[14]. Hence the need to understand the importance of consciousness in bringing about the reality we desire, such as improvement in health status and well-being. The ideal life is living on all levels of consciousness. Chopkra argues that by focusing on one or two levels only, you have caused the others to atrophy and consequently diminish your awareness. In completely expanded awareness, every dimension is accessible. Perhaps this is how we get moments of inspiration that come when we least expect them. Perhaps this is how we know we know.

CHAPTER 6

A NEW PARADIGM

The MIND BODY CONNECTION

The concept that the mind is important in health and illness dates back to ancient times. The words of Hippocrates are in themselves a testimony to the importance of a system that recognised the capacity for healing within.

"The natural healing force within each one of us is the greatest force in getting well".

Energy medicine is an old field of knowledge. It was known to ancient cultures such as Chinese, Hindu and Shamanic healers[1]. Its current revival is based on the needs of an ailing society, who are seeking out more natural ways of healing the body. In western society we are becoming more aware of a discrepancy in our knowledge concerning health and wellbeing. It has become the dogma of a specialist group, without reference to the wealth of knowledge that preceded the current paradigm of health. In the 20th Century with the onset of more serious illnesses such as cancer, and conditions such as Seasonal Affective Disorder (SAD), which is illness from lack of sunlight, we are having to relearn truths that were intuitively understood by our primitive ancestors. In more ancient systems, each person was seen as disparate forms of energy which have to be pulled together and harmonised in accordance with the rhythms of nature[2]. We are having to consider the body holistically, from the perspective of environmental and lifestyle influences and their influence on the energy body which needs to be kept balanced and clear-flowing if optimum health is the goal.

Life is a journey of completeness and the journey back to optimal health is one of consciousness. It is about a new awareness of our own personal inner worlds and how we interact with the world around us. Consciousness is about coming to terms with our personal power and the knowledge that our thoughts have widespread effects. We also need to identify and change outdated belief patterns. In order to do this we need to be aware of the impact of the tribal mind and the complex emotional and psychological forces that impact on our decision making processes[3]. It's also about changing our perception of illness and seeing it in accordance with the new scientific thinking, which views illness as a vibration frequency aberration rather than just as a physical problem. New science has shown that beliefs are an important part of the process as they create our reality and lead us to new levels of consciousness[4]. These new concepts are part of the new body/mind science that will be discussed throughout this chapter.

Within the technological advancement of scientific discovery over the years, the idea of natural healing was somehow lost. The concept of 'getting well' became divorced from human experience and beliefs that our health is determined by our genes promoted a sense of powerlessness in the face of disease. In the West, the notion that mind and body were separate was revived during the Renaissance and Enlightenment eras (1300 to 1600), but was strongly influenced by the protestant reformation of the 16th century and the scientific revolution of the 17th century. The 17th century philosopher and scientist, Rene Descartes, declared them to be two separate entities, with an unbridgeable chasm between the body and spirit and between the brain and the mind[5]. The black and white thinking of this era was reflected in perceptions of the body as well. The latter half of the 18th century and the first half of the 19th century brought an emphasis on technology and manufacturing. This mechanical view of the world was reflected in the understanding of the human person as well. Thus, the notion of the body as a machine which is composed of parts became dominant. If something disturbed it, such as the presence of a pathogen, the machine (body) was deemed to have broken down and could not function properly[6]. All attempts to restore health and abolish illness were deemed to be the responsibility of a group of medical physicians who could mend the machine.

This decline in healing is largely a western phenomenon. The majority of cultures elsewhere in the world continue to use spiritual healing as a normal part of everyday life. It is only relatively recently that people have become aware of a huge imbalance in our western society with respect to the number of escalating illnesses. This has resulted in varying degrees of dissatisfaction with the current regime and a tendency to look outside the dominant paradigm for an answer. The recognition of a need for 'spiritual'/alternative healing has resurfaced in western society. Once again, this was brought about by a change in people's thinking and dissatisfaction with the prevailing paradigm. During the early 1900's a key philosophical perspective on the mind-body connection was offered by Freud, who, although a neurologist, highlighted the significance of psychosomatic medicine. This was followed closely by the post modernism era from 1970's to the present day, which was a time of alternative thought and social and political activism and reform. The prevailing emphasis was focused on de-institutionalisation and individualism. Holism was finally acknowledged, as the connection between mind and body became better understood. For instance, this change of perception led to the discovery of the links between the nervous, endocrine and immune systems[8]. However, in spite of the change in perceptions which have been sweeping into our world, and has been recognised by the scientific community, the outdated medical model persists to the present day.

The Biomedical Model

Scientific beliefs about health and illness are based on Newtonian physics which implies a linear cause and effect model of health without regard to individual differences in outcome. This paradigm of healthcare embraced by western medicine is a century behind the paradigm used in modern physics[9]. It continues to focus on the physiology and chemistry of the body rather than on its energy.

The dominant view of healthcare would have us believe that the bio-medical model of health is sacrosanct and beyond enquiry. This model of medicine has been around since the mid-19th Century and is the dominant model used in the diagnosis of disease. The belief base of this model is that the individual is not responsible for their illnesses and that the mind and body work independently from each other.

It regards illness and disease as an inevitable part of living and ageing, and thereby enhances the notion that the only way forward in a situation of ill health is to seek medical advice and to behave in accordance with this advice, with total disregard for the innate wisdom of the body and mind. It looks for purely physical causes of changes in health and illness, treats the symptoms, and neglects to look for causal factors. An increasing number of scientific and technological discoveries furthered this split and led to an emphasis on disease-based models, pathological changes, and external cures. The dominant model of medicine can be described as a relationship of compliance based on prescribing[10].

In accordance with Newtonian principles, disease and illness are perceived as a malfunction in the system which is 'cured' by providing the body with treatments which aim to change the physical state of the body such as surgery, vaccination, or drugs. From this perspective all illness is viewed as a physical problem requiring physical remedies. Improvements in health are deemed to result only from advancements in medical science. This model does not take into account social factors or individual differences, thereby also excluding prevention of disease as a role in healthcare. It is a Cartesian approach to health in that it perceives mind and body as being mutually exclusive with regard to health factors. However, although science has moved on with regard to physics since Isaac Newton's theory, the delivery of healthcare remains deeply entrenched in Newtonian physics. The dominant view emanating from such principles is that health and disease are determined by a set of genes which are outside one's control. Based on this premise, illnesses like cancer are predetermined by one's genes. Recent research into the biology of human cells have disproved this theory and have rescinded the notion that disease outcome is determined by our genes[11].

In spite of advancements in scientific thought in the post Newton years and the shift in belief patterns to the invisible quantum world of Einstein, such beliefs persist to the present day. We are programmed to believe that illness and disease are an inevitable part of living and ageing, that we are not in control and therefore have no part to play in our own health status. The general consensus being that if one is ill, the body has failed. The only way forward in such a situation is to consult with a physician and to behave in accordance with this advice with total disregard for the innate wisdom of the body and mind. Such conditioning has largely served to support a model of medicine based on outdated concepts of the universe and our supposedly passive role within it.

Complementary medicine believes that our health is dependent on the interaction of body, mind and spiritual energy. When these elements are out of balance the experience is that of illness or disease. Although we may have separate levels of physical, emotional, mental and spiritual health they are all interconnected. We are made up of these four elements. They are inter-dependent and to achieve holistic health we need to give all four consideration in addressing holistic health. We also need to consider the importance of keeping the body in balance with respect to our energy fields. Jan deVries[12] tells us that as we live in an electromagnetic environment, it is important to know how to influence the electromagnetic field of energy in order to restore the body's energy flow. Health is dependent on an unhindered flow of energy that follows the path of the meridians. The energy flows through the body in a circular motion, but as it can only flow in one direction, the laws of polarity between energy and the cells become relevant. Every cell in the body is part of the body's electrical field, so if we obey the laws of nature we are obeying the laws of energy[13].

The World Health Organization (WHO) showed agreement with these principles in their statement that "enjoyment of the highest attainable standard of health is one of the fundamental right of every human being, without distinction of race, religion, political beliefs or economic and social conditions." Within its mandate it declared health as "a complete state of physical, mental, and social well-being and not merely the absence of disease". It would seem that with this definition the WHO were verifying that the biomedical model of health was outdated and inadequate, and was attempting to replace it with what is currently known as the biopsychosocial model. Although both models purport to define health, they have very different agendas. The biomedical model restricts itself to searching for a specific underlying physical cause of disease. In contrast the biopsychosocial model explores all aspects of an illness. The rationale for this model is that health and disease can no longer be considered distinct entities where one exists only in the absence of the other.

It has been suggested that by excluding the social context in which the health problems arise, medical discourse serves to reinforce the dominant ideology and thus, the status quo[14]. A criticism of this approach is that this argument does not link system goals with the doctor's actions such as time pressure on the consultation or the interest of the pharmaceutical industry[15]. However, the importance of including the social context of health has been highlighted in a study of young people with complex neurological disabilities. This research showed that disease outcomes can be moderated or mediated by a number of factors independent of health status, and that having a disability was not equated with health[16].

Some medical practitioners are attempting to adopt a more patient-centred consultation form in their clinical practices but the traditional format of the medical interview does not make it easy. In the current climate of budget led, and unrealistic government-set targets, one could imagine the practical difficulties involved. Surely a case for updating the current system of healthcare with an integrated one? Why then are we still constrained by the dominance of the medical model? Why are we not taking more cognisance of the implications of the WHO statement and its holistic approaches?

"Nothing will change unless or until those who control resources have the wisdom to venture off the beaten path of exclusive reliance on biomedicine as the only approach to health care". – G. L. Engels

Modern medicine denies the value of intuition and emotion and has little time for authority, in spite of being authoritarian. It only values one theory (biomedical) and one way of knowing (empiricism)[17]. However, this dogma is no longer supported by contemporary science. Rather the new biology and new scientific awareness have blown apart such values by demonstrating to us in a scientific way that mind and body are not separate entities and what the mind believes, the body creates[18].

Mind-Body Medicine focuses on the interactions between mind and body and the powerful ways in which emotional, mental, social and spiritual factors can directly affect health. The role of the mind and beliefs in health and illness began to re-enter Western health care in the 20th century, led by discoveries about pain control via the placebo effect and effects of stress on health. Numerous published studies have demonstrated the efficacy of mind-body medicine techniques in lowering blood pressure and stress hormone levels, relieving pain and improving immune functioning, as well as improvements in clinical conditions such as HIV, cancer, insomnia, anxiety, depression and post-traumatic stress disorder[19]. Research by Dr Candace Pert has shown that the body and mind are interconnected and that the 'bodymind' functions as a single psychosomatic network of information molecules which control our health and physiology[20].

How does mind-body medicine work? Mind-body medicine uses the power of thoughts and emotions to influence physical health. It restores the natural wisdom of the body by uncovering the origins of the disease within the conscious and unconscious mind, and consequently reduces stress. When we are physically or emotionally stressed, our body releases stress hormones that can affect all of our systems and organs. Conventional medical practice focuses on the treatment of the disease using drugs and surgery. It would appear that the delivery of health care is undergoing a chrysalis experience and there is a possibility that we may be moving towards a new paradigm or model of health care. From a physics perspective there are new models unfolding based on quantum physics and the new scientific awareness no longer supports a deterministic approach in the arena of healthcare. The findings discussed previously in chapter four, that our thoughts have an effect on our cells and change our biochemistry accordingly, all speak volumes for the importance of expanding the medical model to encompass a more holistic model of care. This begs the question as to how we might expect it to evolve.

Meanwhile there are many impediments to the shift towards a new paradigm, not least of which are deep seated conditioning beliefs about health; ignorance of, or poor exposure to new scientific findings related to health, especially if they challenge the established view; fear about the element of personal responsibility that comes with the new paradigm. All of these are fallouts from the prevailing scientific paradigm related to healthcare.

The time has come for a shift in consciousness both on a personal and on a global level. We have already established the power of thought in changing perceptions and that the current model of health is outdated in terms of its service to maintaining levels of health. We have established that at the quantum level all energy is interconnected. The power of the placebo across the spectrum from personal healing to clinical trials has validated the mind-body connection as a powerful moderator on the pathway to health. But rather than focus on what is wanting in trying to achieve integration, let us focus on the wealth of knowledge and evidence that we have across the healing and medical disciplines

The new Paradigm – an integrated Model of Medicine

Modern medical science has provided remarkable achievements in many areas of healthcare. In the first half of the 20th century, antibiotics transformed the medical landscape by treating life threatening infections such as pneumonia and meningitis. Emergency and critical care doctors represent the best of the "medical model" as they use powerful medications to save lives day after day. Surgeons rely on amazing technology to save lives of trauma patients and those in need of cancer removal and all types of internal repair. We can peer into the body using diagnostic scanning and X-ray techniques with pinpoint precision, while laboratory testing provides detailed explanations of the wondrous natural intelligence of the mind and body. Indeed, no one can doubt the wonders of modern medicine.

However, the future of medicine surely lies in shifting some of the responsibility for healing back to the patient. People need to know more about diet and nutritional biochemistry. But above all, they need to understand how to listen to their own bodies and be prepared to change their lifestyle and mind style. It may well be that as the mind-body healing progresses, medications can be reduced and in some cases the need for drug based medicines, eliminated. In this way people are more likely to heal their diseases and become stronger and wiser in the process.

"Patient empowerment is probably the most philosophically exciting idea to emerge in medicine in recent years. Patients can, and must, be educated to play the primary role in maintaining their own health. I have seen it work and have had the great satisfaction over the past 30 years of helping thousands of individual's live full and active lives." ~ *J. Joseph Prendergast, MD*[21].

Approaching a patient as an individual rather than a collection of body parts is the hallmark of any good medicine. Patient empowerment is the pathway to healing. We empower people by changing their energy field and by raising awareness of the importance of the power of thought. Our thoughts, our beliefs and feelings (emotions) are what are creating our bodies. Consciousness creates the physical molecules. What we think and perceive eventually makes its way down to the cell. The biofields, aura, chakras and meridians that carry the life force energy and make up the human energy body are very important elements in maintaining health. Everything that happens to us, both negative and positive, affects the energy body. It is the negative experiences that create the blockages.

The way forward can only be found through mutual respect and the willingness to embrace the best evidence. For the present, that may be for the most part 'anecdotal 'as expressed by testimonials of those who have returned to good health. Such testimonials are validated by leading edge science and are worth consideration in the light of new scientific discovery.

Let us celebrate the generosity of spirit of those scientists who have taken a risk with their career paths and gone against the dominant paradigm in order to tell the truth. I refer to Bruce Lipton, Candace Perth and Prof Valerie Hunt, Jan de Vries and their contemporaries. Their messages, albeit delivered in different ways in accordance with their expertise, can be summed up as follows: the importance of a rich electromagnetic field for optimal health; body and mind are inseparable due to the fact that the brain is a very powerful force acting upon the body; information from science molds our beliefs about reality and these beliefs create our life patterns. To change a belief we must look at its source and the human experience that validated it. Dr. Hunt[22] says, up until now "many human diseases have been characterized as 'etiology unknown'." In other words, the cause of the disease could not be determined, and therefore the only possible treatment was alleviation of symptoms. But she has determined within her research that physiological symptoms appear because of an energy field disturbance. If we correct the disturbance in the field, the symptoms disappear and the body can heal itself. Whereas, if we treat the symptoms directly, then when a stressful situation aggravates the incoherent energy that is the source of the problem, the disease condition returns.

Medical science is also evolving with new hope for diseases and disorders which were hereto thought of as having no cure. People are living with diseases that would have taken their lives in the past. For instance, Neuroscientist, Prof Geoff Raisman's theory of plasticity which brings hope for Spinal cord injury; Dr Louis Ignarro and his work on l'arginine, and Dr J Prendergast and his work principles of integrative medicine and focus on disease prevention, and of course, Edgar Mitchell, former Astronaut and founder of IONS[23], all who were prepared to risk exclusion from the established scientific opinion for the truth and the good of mankind. Let us celebrate such vision.

The way forward to integrated healthcare is about redressing the balance of power. It is about respecting the collective knowledge that has been passed on from ancestry and it is about the availability of good debate and information regarding the wider view of the management of health and illness. It is also about looking at diseases that remain the corporate preserve of vested interests such as cancer[24]. Philip day suggests that Doctors will continue to struggle with cancer until they accept that a patient is not some collection of malfunctioning cells but a human being out of homeostasis[25]. In western society we are becoming more aware of a discrepancy in our knowledge concerning health and wellbeing. It has become the dogma of a specialist group, without reference to the wealth of knowledge that precedes the current paradigm of health.

CHAPTER 7

Placebo Science - the Role of the Mindset

New levels of consciousness are opening up based on the 'body mind' connection in preserving health. In recent years it has become apparent that the brain is the single most powerful acting force upon the body. The body and mind are inseparable and research has shown this interconnectedness of body mind controls our physiology. For instance, just having an awareness of the innate connection between body, mind and spirit can act as a catalyst for healing[1].

This has been identified in the scientific literature as the "placebo effect" a broad term used to describe a huge range of unexplained phenomena from the use of a sugar pill in drug research to so-called miracle cures. In simple terms, it is a response to a stimulus one believes will work, with the emphasis on one's perception of the efficacy of the stimulus. To date the common thought is that the placebo effect is purely psychological in that it does not represent a real physical change. However there is a lot more going on than is given recognition by the dominant paradigm of health.

Psychologist Ernest Lawrence Rossi reported in his book, that the placebo effect accounts for nearly 56% of the effectiveness of analgesics, like Morphine. This means that when you take a pain killer, more than half of the effect is the direct result of your belief in the pill. And he suggests that effect is not in any way limited to pain killers[2].

Many of the hypotheses that Rossi proposed have now been confirmed by other researchers in their quest for support for the mind/body connection. More recent work carried out by Neuroscientist Jon-Kar Zubieta who explored this effect by giving seven patient volunteers salt solution injections while seven other patients received the real pain killer. The placebo recipients' sense of relief was found to coincide with the release of actual pain-numbing brain chemicals. He argues that this is a much stronger indication of the placebo mind/body connection than the enigmatic changes he previously observed in brain scans[3].

The moderating role of the mind-set (placebo) was supported in further research investigating the benefits of perceived levels of exercise. A marked improvement in physiological measures associated with exercise were found, and these results were independent of actual exercise[4]. This study investigated whether the subject's mind-set (their perceived levels of exercise) could inhibit or enhance the health benefits associated with exercise, independently of actual physical activity. Four weeks after the study, the increase in physiological measures associated with exercise was significant in terms of reducing blood pressure, and although the changes were small the group were found to be significantly healthier. The results of this study show the power of the placebo effect and highlight the role of the mind-set in its ability to enhance health.

A more recent study found that placebos work even when there is no attempt to deceive. However as the sample size was small and limited in scope, the hypothesis would need to be tested in larger trials[5]. These are exciting results, as they once again point to the importance of perception and the role of the brain in changing neurochemistry and consequently in creating and maintaining physical health.

The Science of the Placebo

There has long since been a sense of wonderment regarding how and why placebos work. Dr Joe Dispenza in his book *'You are Placebo'* gives us a first-hand account of the science behind the concept[6]. What is it about the sugar pill or the deception that makes the body respond to suggestibility concerning the outcome? There are three elements involved in the placebo effect: acceptance, belief and surrender and all three need to be subscribed to before the placebo works. For instance, in the case of health, the person must first of all accept the suggestion that the pills will lead to better health, but then there must also be belief that it will work and thirdly, they must surrender to the outcome. With the emotional anticipation of the experience, we become suggestible to the end result. The emotional component is the key. The placebo effect in health is created by a person's consciousness interacting with the autonomic nervous system.

In the case of health, the power of the mind influences the body's physiology, but this happens independently of the conscious mind. Rather, changes happen in the subconscious without the person being consciously aware of how it happened. The system takes over without prompting.

The autonomic nervous system is the seat of subconscious programming and is under the control of the limbic brain. The limbic brain is responsible for subconscious functions such as chemical order and homeostasis for maintaining the body's natural balance. It is also our emotional centre. As we experience different emotions we activate that part of the brain and it creates the corresponding chemical molecules of emotion[7].

When people accept the potential for recovery, they align themselves with a future possible reality and change their minds and brains in the process[8]. They have to get beyond how they are feeling, allowing new thoughts to create new feeling, which in turn reinforces the new thought until it becomes a new state of being[9]. This is the world of quantum possibilities. It is the quantum model that states that all possibilities exist in this moment that allows us to choose a new reality. However, Dispenza says that this is how we create by default as well. If as a quantum observer, you look on your life from the same level of mind every day, you are causing the infinite possibilities of the quantum model to collapse into the same old patterns and consequently, you never effect change. When we focus on something we place our energy there as well and in this way we are affecting matter as well.

Placebos in Medical Trials

There is also much debate regarding the use of Placebos in clinical trials. A review of the Cochrane Central Register of controlled trials between 2001 and 2004 suggested that placebos in general did not have clinically important effects but there were possible beneficial effects on patient reported outcomes, especially pain. However there are reports of studies where placebo was more effective than Prozac for treatment of depression[10].

It seems that the placebo as a dummy pill in studies of new drugs can show an effect of between 35% and up to 75%. A lot of evidence that depression is placebo sensitive has been gathering and Kirsch & Sapirstein analysed 19 clinical trials of anti-depressants and concluded that the expectation of improvement and not adjustments in brain chemistry accounted for 75% of the drug's effectiveness[11]. This work has been viewed with much scepticism and attracted much controversy and hostility not least because of the implications for the future drug market related to prescribing for depression. A further problem of note with drug-related clinical trials is that any trials that do not show a significant difference in favour of the drug are almost never reported on. Also, analysis of randomised control trials published in the Annals of Internal Medicine found that substances used as placebos are not disclosed[12]. Of further note is the fact that there are no measures in place to establish whether these substances could potentially affect the outcome of a trial.

The Nocebo Effect

If a positive perception can have an impact on a person's physiology, it stands to reason that a negative belief may have the opposite effect. Such statements are known as nocebos. Within the medical consultation a nocebo is a negative statements made to a patient following diagnoses of a life threatening illness, usually regarding the closeness of death. We have already established that belief strongly influences perception and affects biology. The placebos and nocebos are about perceptions of power. The former empowers the patient while the latter can be described as a type of programming of people into believing that they are powerless. Dr Andrew Weil[13], describes the nocebo as a type of medical hexing and compares the outcome of a nocebo to the outcome on a victim of the practice of ancient cultures, who when 'cursed' by a shaman or witch doctor, withdrew from society, stopped eating, weakened and died. The prediction of a negative outcome may unintentionally be a psychological defence for the physician against uncertainty. If the patient recovers, the physician can be pleasantly surprised and take credit, whereas if the patient gets worse or dies, the physician is still in control having predicted the outcome.

Although medical nocebos may be based on experience of disease outcomes, words are powerful conduits of emotional states. Dr Candice Pert in her work has demonstrated that our moods and understanding are not just electrical impulses in the brain but are responsible for the chemicals that are released into our bloodstream. As the usual effect of medical hexing is a state of despair, it would be reasonable to assume that the accompanying emotion would affect the body at a cellular level, producing the chemicals which would not be conducive to a return to optimal health. Dr Pert explains that the biochemicals produced are neuropeptides and receptors which are messengers carrying information to link the major systems of the body into one unit which she calls the 'body mind'[14].

Perhaps it is time to reconsider the outcome of the nocebo because it is the current perceived practice in hospitals, clinics and surgeries. Information about estimated time of survival should not be divorced from information provided by the new science regarding the capacity of the body for self-healing, which empowers the patient to engage in the process required. Weill suggests that in the delivery of nocebos, consultants are taking on the role of 'high priests' of technological medicine, brought about by an illusion of control over life and death, while agreeing that most medical hexing derives from a position of thoughtlessness rather than intention.

The importance of giving people hope has been emphasised by the work of recent scientists. Quantum physics has taught us that we create what we believe in our minds. Energy follows thought and what we fear we attract. Our physiology and behaviour patterns conform to the truths of the central voice, be they constructive or destructive beliefs.

Critics of the 'mind-body' connection influence can no longer justify the argument that 'hard' evidence is lacking to support belief that what we think or perceive can affect our ability to deal with major challenges whether with respect to disease or how we function in our daily lives[15]. Current scientific evidence about the biochemical influences of consciousness and awareness which give credibility to the mind-body model are based on quantum physics. Scientists discovered that atoms could be broken down and that the subatomic particles which collectively formed the atoms, are composed of pure energy.

As already discussed in chapter 2, at the quantum level everything that exists in the Universe is vibrating and oscillating at different rates. All atoms in the elemental world emit various electromagnetic energies, and can give off invisible fields of energy at different frequencies. For instance, just as invisible radio waves carry frequencies with different information encoded in it, each frequency carries specific diverse information[16]. All these fields are different energy patterns giving off information at the atomic level. From a quantum perspective, atoms are vibrating fields of energy. So, the physical universe shares a field of information that unifies matter and energy so intimately that it is impossible to think of them as separate entities. It is a field of information that goes beyond space and time which is made up of consciousness which is thought, and energy which is frequency (the speed at which things vibrate).

According to Quantum physics we can observe ourselves in a new future by invoking the expectation that the desired reality will occur and by emotionally embracing the outcome as if the desired future is happening in the present moment. This conditions the body to believe that it is in that specific future, in the present moment. Once we fix our attention we place energy there as well. When we change our energy to alter a belief or perception we are increasing the frequency of the atoms and molecules of our physical body. This has the effect of amplifying the energy field so that we are becoming more energy (wave) and less matter (particle). In this way, using our consciousness we are creating more energy so that matter can be lifted to a new frequency so that the body responds to a new mind[17].

New leading edge research based on quantum physics discovered anomalies in the teachings of conventional medicine that our biology is determined by our genes[18]. The basis of this belief system renders us powerless with regard to health and matters of survival. This model of health continues to focus on the physiology and chemistry of the body rather than its energy.

The work of Dr Candace Perth demonstrates that our moods and thoughts are not just electrical impulses in the brain but that they are also coded in the neuropeptides that are released into the bloodstream[19], the thoughts are converted into signals sent to the cells to coordinate their function with regard to the nature of the thoughts. Thus the importance of living in a world with perceptions that are not fear based.

Current advances in technology may be partly responsible for the shift in consciousness towards better management of health. The information on managing illness and disease made available through the global media may put people in a better position to make informed lifestyle and medical decisions; knowledge is power. For instance, there is a trend towards people assuming more responsibility for managing their own health. People are more informed about the benefits of nutrition, exercise, and how to manage stress as well as how they can take care of themselves when they are ill. More people are turning to natural remedies to prevent illness as well as to complement orthodox medical methods of treatment. This practice may be due as much to the availability of information as to a disenchantment with current medical practices. Fears about the harmful side effects of some prescription drugs are prompting people to seek alternatives whenever possible.

Given the prevailing view that all matters relating to health and healthcare are the concern of a distinct group of health professionals it would be reasonable to conclude that such conditioning would lead to perceptions of disempowerment. The power of personal constructs like 'self-efficacy' and 'perceptions of control' have all been well established in the medical literature within the framework of the biomedical model so it is not rocket science to expect that such beliefs would have consequences for perceptions of health and indeed for health status. In fact there is a considerable literature linking self-perceptions of health with mortality[20]. Perhaps in future such outcomes can be interpreted within the framework of mind body science and its relationship with health.

It may be that the influence of commercial interests over medical practice are reinforcing the doctor/ patient power relationships of the dominant paradigm as they are the mainstay of western medical practices. For instance, the growth of the use of medicines over a 50 year period shows an increase in the percentage of gross national product from 4.5% in 1950's to 16% in 2006 making healthcare a big industry of which the pharmaceutical industry plays a major role [21].

Nickey Britten in her book on Medicines and Society highlights the effects of the divorce of patients' perspectives on illness and drug licensing from those of the system. She discusses tensions between patients and health providers as a colonization of the 'lifeworld', where the term 'lifeworld' defines the needs and concerns of lay people. She defines the 'system' as governmental health policies, licensing of drugs and the influence of the pharmaceuticals, all of which have consequences for current health practice.

Britten also noted a neglect by the 'system' of other ways of managing health and illness as well as a tendency to over-emphasise the benefits of pharmaceutical treatments rather than their harms. Conversely there is tendency to pay more attention to the 'harms' of complementary medicine than to their benefits. We suggest that this unequal balance of power (colonization) is another factor in reinforcing the dominant paradigm and another reason why we have not seen much of a shift towards a more holistic model of healthcare.

IMPLICATIONS OF A PARADIGM SHIFT

Historically scientists who have challenged the established paradigm have faced numerous obstacles to gain acceptance, even at the risk of their own lives -for instance, Copernicus and Leonardo, in the 15th and 16th century. It seems that not much has changed in this regard even with advances in science. Many eminent scholars with outstanding academic records who ventured to investigate for the common good, the mind/body influence (consciousness) in health and disease, have been sidelined by their peers as well as by professional and scientific institutions[22].

Health is about maintaining the natural equilibrium of body, mind and soul. Healing is the process whereby the rifts between body, mind and soul are repaired, and well-being is about living up to your capabilities, being whole and flourishing[23]. Let us now move on to seeing how this works out in practice.

PART II

HiddenMind in Practice

PART TWO - Chapter 8

INTRODUCING MERIDIAN
AND CORRECTIONAL SYSTEMS

The HiddenMind investigative programme views the human body as a naturally self–correcting system when given the opportunity to do so. It seeks to explore and unlock the hidden potential of the human mind to restore and regenerate the entire energetic structure of the human person. It does not diagnose any specific conditions but aims to tap into the body's own healing resources in order to return the body to its natural condition of optimum health. This is done with the help of the subconscious mind and by correction of the body's electrical /energy systems. The aims of the programme are to return the body to a state of improved mental, physical and spiritual wellbeing.

It has been established that the human body and the energy field that surrounds it is made up of electromagnetic energy and this has been discussed throughout part 1. We have also discussed the evidence that pathology alters the bio-magnetic field and that such changes can be detected in the energy field before the physical symptoms present in the body[1] The energy system of the body consists of an integration of a network of powerful and effective healing techniques that work by rebalancing the life force energy within and around the human body. These intelligent life energies take a number of forms and are normally in a state of continuous flow throughout the body. Similar to nervous impulses, they travel through a system of definite channels and in recent research, scientists measuring variations in electrical skin resistance have extensively mapped these channels or meridians as they are more commonly known. The biofield which we have discussed in earlier chapters is described as an energetic matrix that surrounds the human body which directly links the cellular activity with the meridian pathways. Our health is dependent on a good energy balance and on an unhindered flow of energy that follows the path of the meridian

The meridians are an integral part of the body's energy system. They comprise a network of energy channels and can be thought of as the body's energy bloodstream[2]. Each one passing through one side of the body has a mirror image on the other side. If the flow of energy becomes imbalanced, stagnant or disturbed in any way it automatically affects not just the physical body by disrupting its function and allowing disease to set in, but also the mental, spiritual and emotional aspects as well. Keeping the universe and the body in harmony is important as blockages in the energy system if not balanced, can manifest as pathology. Energy conditions are usually the forerunners of more serious problems, hence the importance of detecting the disharmony before it causes further problems[3]. The work of cell biologist Dr Bruce Lipton[4] supports this view in that he had observed that diseased tissue emits its own unique energy signature which is different to that emitted by surrounding health cells.

The body contains fourteen meridians comprising twelve pairs as well as two special meridians known as vessels. The bio-energy flows along the twelve main meridians, which are symmetrical on each side of the body, each pair relating to a specific organ. The two special meridians known as the Governing and Conception vessels are very important because they contain acupuncture points which are independent of the twelve principle meridians. They also have a role in positioning the other twelve, giving them the human shape and forming the basis of the meridian structure within the body. In fact, we could say that there is a single meridian running throughout the whole body as all meridians are connected to each other and are flowing into one another. They are in fact paired, giving twenty four separate pathways. Together they constitute the energy system of the body which works to maintain the health of the organism. These meridians are the pathways through which the universal or life force energy circulates. Meridian Therapy assumes that a disorder within a meridian creates disharmony along that meridian pathway and can sometimes indicate disharmony in the meridian's connecting organ. Knowledge of the meridians can help therapists to have a more in-depth understanding of the disease pathway[5].

The meridians can be used for a better understanding of health conditions. One can path of each meridian as it transverses the body in order to assess whether the chronic symptoms lie within the pathway of the dysfunctional meridian. The flow of energy happens in specific cycles within a twenty-four hour period. The energy flows at a maximum level for a period of two hours in each meridian and at minimum level twelve hours later. The specific two hour period of energy flow associated with each meridian and its corresponding body organ, is often referred to in the literature as 'the body-clock'.

For instance, knowledge of the associated time frame can act as a reference with regard to symptoms experienced during a specific time period, and thus can be an indication of blocked energy in a specific meridian and its associated organ. The meridian system can also help us to understand why many disease symptoms are located in certain parts of the body when the originating cause is actually a weakness or inflammation of an organ in another part. For instance, the site of the pain can indicate which meridian is congested; pains in the index finger refer to the large intestine meridian[6]. If there is congestion along the paths of any of the meridians, this will interfere with the energy flow of the body; the balance of the body will be disturbed and unless this imbalance is addressed, it will inevitably result in disease.

Encoded within its electrical pattern the energy field contains information that can be regarded as the original "blue print" of the person. It also contains information that accurately reflects a person's current physical, emotional, mental and spiritual state. This blueprint is stored in the subconscious mind which holds details of the personal history of each individual. The subconscious mind can be contacted via the practice of the science of Kinesiology, and information regarding the health status of the body can be extracted using this method.

Western medicine recognises a nervous system and a circulatory system within the human body but focuses on the structure and function of each individual organ and treats each one as separate from all the other organs. This philosophy is based purely on intervention by means of surgery or drug therapy and much of the wisdom of the body as a holistic entity has little place in modern medicine. On the other hand, the HiddenMind programme and other ancient healing systems work on the principle that the structure of an organ consists of the organ and the meridian responsible for nourishing it, as well as how that organ relates to and is influenced by, the other organs and their meridians. All healing that takes place in alternative or complementary medicine is electromagnetic. There is a consciousness of healing based on the rediscovery of ancient truths concerning the body's amazing ability to correct its own maladies with non-invasive procedures such as, changes in lifestyle, nutrition and accessing the corrective system of the hidden mind and bioenergy program. In ancient civilizations, healing was part of the fabric of everyday society and the healers and leaders knew how important it was for physical, emotional and spiritual health that the body's energy frequencies were kept in balance and fully attuned. Any frequency malfunction in the body's electrical system can be ascertained through the HiddenMind programme with the use of the system of Kinesiology and can be corrected accordingly. How this is achieved will be discussed in more detail in the following chapters.

CHAPTER 9

THE HIDDEN MIND CORRECTIVE SYSTEM

RESTORING THE ENERGY MATRIX

The three main energising systems of the human body are the Meridians, the Chakras and the Auric Fields. These collectively comprise twenty eight cardinal frequencies consisting of fourteen meridians, seven chakras and seven auric fields, all of which contribute in specific ways to maintaining the homeostasis of the energy system. The ancient healers and leaders knew how important it was for physical, emotional and spiritual health that these cardinal frequencies were kept in balance and were fully attuned. If they are damaged through emotional or physical shock, the subconscious mind has to be consulted as it holds all of the blueprint information about the body's energy pathways. The fourteen meridians as discussed in the last chapter, provide the framework for the energy body; the seven chakra frequencies are the suppliers of energy to the meridians and organs and the seven auric fields perform the role of communicators and protectors to the body.

The auric fields, which are different from the aura, are the body's main protective system. They act as two way antenna, bringing in energy from the environment to the chakras and sending energy out from them. They act as protectors of the electrical systems by filtering out any harmful energies and bringing in energies that are needed, whereas the chakras provide energy to specific organs. The energy taken in by the chakras is dispersed by the meridians for use throughout the body. The energy frequencies of the chakras can be altered by shock, causing problems in the body. However, any dysfunction in the chakras can be easily corrected with the HiddenMind programme.

Frequency malfunction in the body's electrical system can also be corrected via the Hiddenind programme using techniques based on the system of kinesiology. For instance, if any of the twenty-eight cardinal frequencies become altered, for example if a meridian becomes shortened in length due to a malfunction, then the sub-conscious will align the body to the shortened meridian causing the physical structure to warp in order to compensate. The sub-conscious will use the body's own muscles and bone structure to realign the physical structure to the now imperfect framework. If this is not corrected, illness and in some cases, pain, will follow as nerve structure will be damaged due to the misalignments. This is about maintaining the integrity of the body. If the matrix remains in an altered state, then the body remains in an altered state until corrected.

In the following chapters we will explain in detail the trajectory of the hidden mind bio-energy and investigative programme as well as the role of the subconscious within the framework of the programme. The subconscious mind stores the personal history of each individual. It allows the body to function on an everyday basis and also facilitates access to information concerned with the wellbeing of the body.

Blockages and malfunctions in the electrical system of our bodies can happen at any stage and can be due to physical or emotional shock, altered positions of spinal vertebrae or various environmental factors. However it can also be the result of experiences during the birthing process, even in adults. For instance, misalignment of the sphenoid, occiput, or one or both temporal bones at birth are thought to be the prime causes of dyslexia and other learning difficulties. Dyslexia can also be caused by a shock in later life, causing the left and right brain to be shocked out of integration. However, the effects of the condition if caused later in life is not as serious.

In order to understand the causes of Dyslexia, ADD, ADHD, Dyspraxia, Asperger's syndrome, Learning Difficulties and the Autistic Spectrum, it is necessary to understand the problems that can arise in the very early stages of a child's life. These critical stages start at the moment of conception until the cranial bones integrate at about twenty months old. Conception, time spent in the womb and birth lay the foundation for what we experience as adults. Everything experienced by the mother becomes the experience of the foetus including the effects of the foods ingested by the parent and the effects of shock or stress.

For instance, if the pregnancy is not planned and is resented, the resulting emotion can be experienced by the unborn child. This emotion can cause interference in the electrical systems of the unborn child and in later life can result in dissatisfaction with life in general, loss of the ability to trust other people, and difficulty in finding emotional fulfilment. It is surprising how many adults have presented at the clinic for correction who were acutely aware of such a scenario, and most reported that it had an effect on their relationship with one or other parents throughout their lives. The HiddenMind correction programme deletes the memory associated with this type of scenario, as well as restoring any damage to the electrical system of the now adult person.

More recent research has highlighted the implications of birth shock resulting from difficult and prolonged births, such as, vacuum, forceps delivery and C-section births. Stressful births can strain the neck and head, causing interference in the nerve signals between the brain and digestive system. Children who were C-section births have been found to be more susceptible to allergies than babies born via the natural birthing process.

Another factor related to the birthing process which needs consideration in relation to ongoing health and wellbeing is the impact of the birthing process on the life force energy. A child can lose a certain percentage of the life force energy during the birthing experience and this can have an impact on the wellbeing of the child in later years. This anomaly is always tested within the HiddenMind protocol in order to ascertain whether the presenting symptoms are in any way related to this phenomenon. The subconscious mind of the child is questioned through the medium of vibration kinesiology, to indicate if the life force energy one hour before birth was at maximum level. In our investigative protocol we use a score of 3600 as evidence of maximum life force. For instance, if the life force energy is down to 1800 one hour post birth, this means that the child lost half of its life force energy during the birthing process. The subconscious mind of a child can be questioned as to whether any of that life force energy has been recovered, but more often than not, it has not. This also adds to the emotional shock experienced by the child and further disrupts the electrical systems of the body, resulting in problems such as Dyslexia, ADD, ADHD and other such lifestyle complications.

The correct development of a child between conception and birth is very important for later development. There are many ways that an unborn child can be affected in utero. The ones of most concern are those that affect the three electrical systems; namely, the meridians, the chakras and the auric fields. These problems usually manifest either as, meridian malfunctions or perpetuating gene faults.

The meridians are the ones that are mostly affected while in utero. They can be affected by bloodline or hereditary factors in the form of meridian malfunctions or perpetuating gene faults. These malfunctions can come from the mother's or father's side or sometime from both and they can affect the child at any stage. However, it is our experience with the HiddenMind programme, that this mostly occurs in utero in the first month of the second trimester, which is the fourth month in utero and in the seventh month.

It is important to understand what meridians are and what their functions are in order to understand how they can be damaged. We have already established that a meridian is a pathway of energy that contains blueprint information about the developing shape of the foetus. We know that there are at least fourteen meridians, seven on either side of the body and that it is very important to have them functioning correctly for the proper development of the foetus in utero and afterwards for the ongoing correct functioning of all faculties throughout life.

When the subconscious mind becomes aware that the foetus has inherited a negative trait from either parent in the form of a negative emotion, an anxiety state, a negative thought form, a belief system or a phobia, it causes the meridians to partially or fully cease their function in order to protect them from further overload. This can be experienced as severe emotional shock by the developing foetus and the subconscious mind will not permit these meridians to continue to function until the emotional shock is identified and corrected.

Perpetuating Gene Fault:

A perpetuating gene fault is also a fault emanating from an ancestor which can also affect the meridians and the kundalini (the first Auric Field). This in turn will cause electro physical shock affecting the development of the bones of the skull and spine while in utero; and more so after birth, when the cranial bones are reintegrating. For instance if a foetus has a meridian malfunction affecting him from his father's or mother's bloodline and the meridians on the right side are affected in what we call specific order, then the governing, lung, spleen, liver, gall bladder, large intestine and kidney meridians can all be compromised causing health problems to manifest in the body.

Both meridian malfunctions and perpetuating gene faults are corrected by a corrective sound practitioner by tracing back through the family tree to find the originator of the fault. This can be via a living family member or it could be traced back to an ancestor eight or ten generations back through the bloodline; a physical or emotional trauma can pass through the bloodline affecting all the generations and now affecting the latest new arrival in the family. As it passes through each generation it can become more intense due to a possible build up as each generation accumulates their own gene faults. It is important to note at this stage that the meridian structure is also present in the unfertilized ova. The female ovary has 5,000 unfertilised eggs as ova. Each ovum has fourteen meridians structures carrying information from generations in the past, generations into the future and generations latterly. This means that a child in the womb can be affected by his first cousin's great-grandfather. A child can also experience emotional shock via the experiences of the mother. If the pregnant mother has a physical trauma or is living in an abusive environment, then the foetus she is carrying can also register these shocks in their subconscious. These faults can affect the development of several meridians on one side of the body. The consequences of this are enormous. First it can cause problems at birth, resulting in caesarean section or difficult births involving suction or forceps deliver. Over the nine months in utero the primary energy pattern is called the kundalini. This is the unfolding shape of the child and the continuing unfolding shape of a human being. However, if the meridians are not functioning properly, the potential for ongoing development may be compromised.

It takes 7 - 9 months after birth for the two hemispheres of the brain to fully integrate and another further 9 - 12 months for the cranial bones to integrate and articulate. If the subconscious mind of the child has registered emotional shock as a result of hereditary problems in the womb, or if the mother has experienced physical, mental or environmental shock during pregnancy, the unborn foetus can register this in their subconscious minds. If children have experienced a difficult birth, such as, induction, forceps, suction, caesarean, or shock from the side effects of vaccinations, these can be the underlying features which need a correction. In this situation the subconscious mind of the child will hold back information from one of the hemispheres so that they cannot fully integrate. This in turn has repercussions for spinal development and the cranial sacral pulse.

The first bone that connects the skull to the spine is the occipital. This has to position itself properly to allow the cavity to develop in order to allow the brainstem to fully integrate into the spine. This is the core of the spinal cord and nervous system. If this bone is misaligned than there is interference in one or all of those systems. The cerebro spinal fluid is created in the ventricles of the brain and pumped up and down the spine and around the body via the articulation of the cranial plates. The sacrum and associated vertebrae, pump the fluid up the spine into the brain. If the occiput and atlas and associated vertebrae are not in the correct physical position or the correct electrical fields, this pumping action cannot happen at the proper pace. This can cause even further problems and, at a later stage, can be the basis of special need conditions such ADD, ADHD, Learning Difficulties and Autistic Spectrum disorder.

Birth - 9 Months:

This is a very important developmental stage because during this stage the cranial bones begin to integrate and the two brain hemispheres to integrate to form one brain. It is through the acts of suckling and crying by the new-born that the cranial bones establish their integration patterns. Between the seven to nine month periods the hemispheres of the brain should integrate to the corpus callosum which is the conductor between both brain hemispheres.

The corpus callosum connects both brains and billions of neurological exchanges occur every second. It is interesting to note here that the corpus callosum is a third longer in females giving them their multitasking ability, their more than one hundred and eighty degree peripheral vision and early learning ability. If any of the faults already mentioned are present and the subconscious mind is registering a state of shock then one or other of the hemispheres will not integrate one hundred per cent.

If the child is badly shocked only one hemisphere may integrate or connect to the corpus callosum but not at maximum, for example sometimes it will be connected at only forty percent. This can set off a chain of events which can lead to a special needs diagnosis later in early childhood. It is interesting to note that the side effects of vaccines can also add to the level of shock experienced by the child. In cases where the HiddenMind programme indicates shock from the side effects of vaccines, the parents are informed and a correction can be applied to delete the memory. One of the benefits of the programme is if there is any memory of emotional shock lurking in the subconscious mind, the hidden mind corrective sound protocol will delete it. This correction is carried out at an energetic level and is always advantageous to the child.

As Therapists of HiddenMind Investigative and Corrective Sound Protocol we leave the decision to vaccinate up to the parents and if any problems arise as a result of the vaccines we will endeavour to clear those memories.

Lung Meridian

(Yun Men) LU2

(Zhongf Fu) LU1

(Chi Ze) LU5

(Kong Zui) LU6

(Lie Que) LU7

(Yu Ji) LU10

(Shao Shang) LU11

(Tai Yuan) LU9

CHAPTER 10

THE HIDDENMIND INVESTIGATIVE PROTOCOL

This treatment differs from the bio-energy treatment in that there is a verbal questioning of the subconscious mind of the client to identify the hidden causes of diseases and symptoms. Questions come in the form of statements that are designed to elicit exact information stored in the subconscious mind of the client in regard to their physical, mental, emotional, chemical and spiritual being. The subconscious of the client is recruited as it is accepted that the subconscious contains innate information about a person's health that cannot be elicited through normal scientific medical investigative procedures.

The subconscious could be likened to the internet or the body's invisible library. In order to access the internet one needs to have a computer and use a search engine to access information. The medium used by the HiddenMind programme to access the information stored in the subconscious mind, is dowsing. Dowsing is the art of using a pendulum as a medium to indicate the truth or non-truth of a question or statement, which is directed to the subconscious mind of the client during the correction process. During a therapist's training an agreement is set up between the subconscious mind of the therapist and their own pendulum as regards the directions the pendulum will spin to indicate a true or false, or yes and no answer. Dowsing is a bio-feedback mechanism and each therapist through intensive training and experience is confident that the investigative protocol will elicit the most accurate information the subconscious mind of the client will allow.

The HM therapist works on the premise that a client's subconscious mind knows the maximum function and frequency of the client's physical and non-physical being and therefore can indicate to the therapist when any energetic or biological system is functioning at less than maximum. One can also dowse to find out what percentage out of possible maximum frequency is involved. The HiddenMind protocol also uses the pendulum while touching certain points on the body to indicate the presence of viruses, pathogens, toxins and maladies such as candida and glandular fever.

Before a treatment starts an agreement must be set up between the therapist and the conscious and subconscious mind of the client. After the therapist explains the overall procedure to the client permission to investigate is asked of the subconscious mind of the client. This is done by means of making a statement and the therapist's pendulum indicates if permission is given. If permission is refused this can be due to possible sabotage of the investigation and the source of this sabotage needs to be identified and deleted. Subconscious opposition on the part of the client to the investigation may be due to strict religious beliefs, being very skeptical of the process, having a sense of being pushed or coerced into the treatment by a friend or relative or having a feeling of being let down by other treatments. There can be any number of reasons for sabotage and experience has shown that they can usually be identified and resolved. If not, then this may not be the most appropriate time to carry out the protocol.

The investigative protocol begins with physical observation of the client in a standing position. If the client has mobility or skeletal problems and cannot stand then the observation is done in whatever position is most suitable, whether sitting or lying down. The objective of the physical observation is to determine whether there is any physical deviation in the structure of the body such as, one shoulder being lower than the other, head tilted towards one side, one leg shorter than the other, deviations in the spine such as scoliosis, kyphosis or lordosis. The eyes are then checked for deviations like strabismus, squint or lazy eye. There are techniques used by the therapist with the use of a finger in front of the eyes in order to elicit responses which can determine if the eyes are functioning binocularly or have irregular deviations. These eye tests can also indicate whether the hemispheres of the brain are in alignment with the eyes. This test can also give an indication if dyslexia or learning difficulties are present. The client is then observed in a lying down position and further structural deviations may be observed. Physical deviations can indicate that there are underlying energetic blockages and these can correct spontaneously during the investigative protocol.

The second stage of the protocol checks whether the brain hemispheres have integrated fully as this function is paramount to good health. If one of the hemispheres is not integrated this can indicate previous physical or emotional shock. In the case of children with special needs this can be an indicator of pre-birth or birth shock.

The HiddenMind protocol is designed to continue investigating until all stored information is accessed, all probable malfunctions have been tested and the source of the problem has been identified. The subconscious will indicate to the therapist when sufficient information has been exposed to the conscious mind for a correction to take place.

The third stage of the protocol involves an investigation of the cranial plates to see if they are articulating correctly; if not this can be indicative of hyperactivity. In this condition, the cranio-sacral fluid pump can be negatively affected which can cause too much adrenalin being pumped into the brain. In order for the cranio-sacral pump to work at optimal level there is a requirement for the vertebrae of the spine to be in their correct physical position and in their correct electrical fields. This is also determined through statements to the subconscious. It is also important to determine if there is reflux in the cerebrospinal fluid.

The final stage of the protocol involves investigating the three electrical systems, consisting of seven chakras, fourteen meridians and the seven auric fields. These systems are the software that connect the physical body to the non-physical world around it. As already discussed, they are the transmitters and receivers of information and frequencies to and from our immediate environment. As our organs and cells are nourished by these electrical systems it is important that they are functioning at their optimal frequency. Only the subconscious can elicit the information regarding their frequency. If we take the meridians for instance, the investigative protocol could track the source of the frequency malfunction back as far as one of the months in utero and this in turn could be sourced back several generations on the mother's or father's bloodline. The faults that carry through the bloodlines are called meridian malfunctions or perpetuating gene faults. These can be unresolved emotional or physical traumas which were imprinted into the subconscious minds of the family ancestors and these unresolved traumas can cause emotional shock to a child. If these faults are not identified and have not been resolved, they can cause interference in the development of the child at a later stage in their life.

If a child is born with damage to the electrical systems, this means that the birthing process is incomplete and there is unfinished business between the mother and the child. The birthing process itself can be emotionally traumatic and especially so if the child has an excessively long and difficult birth and/or is born via caesarean section. If the cord has been cut too quickly this can also be an issue which needs to be identified and corrected. If pre-birth or birth shock or both is experienced, the child's life force energy is lowered, negatively affecting the child's further development. The mother will unconsciously hold this lost life-force energy and this can be returned to the child once identified by the hidden mind program.

The sixth auric field of the mother connects automatically to the child's energy system and also to all family members alive and passed away. The child can demonstrate a loss of energy metaphorically in showing traits of abnormal behavior, learning difficulties, tantrums, rage, eating disorders, and difficulties in communicating and in numerous other ways. A child that constantly clings to the mother, afraid to let her out of its sight, is trying to tell the mother that there is programming to be returned to the child. The investigative protocol pays special attention to these scenarios as the subconscious mind has to be recruited to elicit this information. Only then can a reconnection between the mother and child's energy be fully made and thus completing the birthing process and the child's ability to self-correct and develop properly.

A lot of unresolved problems in children can be carried into adulthood, hence the need to investigate fully back to the birthing process. For instance, when treating adults with depression and mood disorders the investigative protocol scans the subconscious mind for memories of negative emotions, negative thought forms, anxiety, negative belief systems and any other hidden memories of traumatic events that may be negatively affecting them. In some situations friends or family members can be negatively affecting the client through negative thought forms or anxiety states. The subconscious mind has to be recruited to identify and delete these features. The investigative protocol also makes statements which are directed at the subconscious mind in order to determine whether the biological function of the organs are vibrating at the full capacity (100%) and if not, it determines what percentage frequency they are currently operating at, in order to bring them up to optimal frequency level. The investigative protocol also indicates the percentage of life-force energy available to the organs.

The chakras are vortexes of energy that download vital life-force energy to the meridians, and the organs and cells and indeed all systems of the body. The chakras also can store negative emotions which can also be stored in the gross organs of the body. Meridians can also store negative emotional debris in the organs to which they are connected. For instance the kidney can house the negative emotion of fear, the liver anger, the pancreas and spleen anxiety, the lungs grief and depression, the gall bladder rage and the heart, hate and resentment. This negative emotional debris is often the source of disease and may also be responsible for organs not functioning at their optimal level.

The auric fields are also transmitters, receivers, filters and protectors of energies and vibrations in our environment. It is also important to ascertain if these fields are all functioning at maximum levels. If the auric fields have a low frequency they start to break down and energies enter the body unprocessed and unfiltered. This can cause anxiety in the physical body as the body can feel under threat and panic can set in. This in turn has a knock on effect on the body by creating a rush of stress hormones. If the client's energies are broken down the client can feel constantly on edge and very uncomfortable in tense situations. Auric fields also protect the body from viruses and pathogens and the client whose auric fields are broken down are much more likely to be negatively affected.

Viruses and pathogens are identified by touching certain indicator points on the body while simultaneously making a statement to the subconscious mind of the client for verification of the presence or a memory of a virus or pathogen. To clear those you have to identify how long they are present, if they are high or low grade, which organs they are affecting and the number of electrical systems affected. The subconscious mind is also questioned in order to identify if mold toxins are present as these can impact negatively on the immune system. Intolerances to substances is something that affects many clients. This can be something as simple as the colour of the dye in an item of clothing or an allergenic reaction to a cleaning substance being used regularly. The subconscious mind can identify these reactive substances if asked the correct questions.

Another unique feature of the investigative protocol is to discern whether symptoms are due to a psychosomatic cause. Psychosomatic illnesses arise when the brain of the client is partially or fully responsible for creating the illness or illnesses in the body. This can be caused by the presence of unresolved dangerous emotions like rage and anger which are buried in the subconscious mind and are too traumatic to be allowed to surface to the conscious mind. Therefore the conscious mind is bypassed and the brain creates a specific type of drama in the physical body to create a distraction in order to camouflage these negative emotions. The brain creates a process called ischemia which is a deprivation of blood and oxygen to nerves and muscles, causing muscle inflammation and inflamed joints, even causing subluxations in vertebra and prolapses in disc structures which can be seen in scans and x-rays.

Dr. John Sarno in his book *The Divided Mind* says that a huge number of people with chronic pain in the lower and upper back and neck as well as others with headaches, hypertension, irritable bowel syndrome and fibromyalgia, have created these realities as a distraction from underlying past emotions, or from more recent ones. The investigative protocol identifies features of these emotions such as how long they are present, how they were caused, how they have affected the electrical systems, particularly the meridians and the chakras, and the immune system. When sufficient information is presented by the subconscious of the client this has a diluting effect on the intensity of the underlying emotion. This has the effect of allowing the emotion to enter the conscious mind and the brain can now stop creating ischemia, allowing the symptoms to dissipate. This process can take time and can require several treatments.

Another interesting feature of the investigative protocol is the ability to investigate the client's Telios or measure of the degree to which one is getting the most out of life; whether one is in the right environment, living in the right area, has the right job, has a good relationship partner etc. If a person's Telios is below maximum then an investigation is initiated within the Hiddenmind protocol to see which aspect or features of the person's life needs attention. The client can usually identify with the results of the investigation, given that it is their own subconscious mind which has released the information. Once all the relevant information has been documented using the investigative protocol, an initial correction has already taken place and in addition, a new mind-body reconnection has taken place the effects of which can be seen in the physical body.

The Tibetan Horn being used during sound therapy

Corrective Sound Protocol

The corrective sound protocol which is part of the Hiddenmind Investigative programme involves the use of special sound frequencies or harmonics as part of the overall corrective procedures. The instruments used are of Tibetan and Balinese origin and come from the Vedic / Hindu heritage. These sound frequencies are a synthesis of chakra bowls, chakra bells, copper horns, symbols, gongs and an array of oriental instruments that have been used for thousands of years in the monasteries by priests and holy men to transfer vital information from the subconscious mind to the conscious mind and to the biological and physiological reality of the person.

Sound carries powerful frequencies that influence our mood and emotions. When we hear a beautiful piece of music be it vocal or instrumental it can have an immediate effect, uplifting our mood and bringing about a state of great joy or sadness. It is said that when Albert Einstein heard Yehudi Menuhin playing the violin at a concert he was so overwhelmed with emotion that he said, "there is a God".

The sounds used in the HiddenMind Protocol have the precise pitch and harmonics to amplify the body's energy and frequencies up to maximum level in order to bring them into its present corrective state. For instance, if a meridian is damaged at 4 months in utero and is only developed up to 30% of its potential and that person is now forty years old it takes a huge frequency jump to restore that to normal. It is now known that the subconscious mind has an incredible capacity to utilise sound frequency in order to influence the regeneration of cells, organs, bone, tissue, and blood. Sound frequencies can dramatically improve healing rates and restore homeostasis and balance. These frequencies have been used for decades by different practitioners around the world to improve neural development in special needs children, in particular using Mozart's music. The sound frequencies used in HiddenMind are played both individually and in an eclectic form. A combination of special sound frequencies and the spoken word are used to correct meridians and have a powerful ability to transform negative emotional charges present in the organs and meridians.

According to the mathematical 'String theory', (which attempts to reconcile quantum mechanics and general relativity), the frequency of the vibrations of each string determines their individual properties. This is manifested in the observation of particles which exhibit identical reactions to other particles even though they are separated by vast distances. This concept claims that everything in our universe from the planets swirling through space, through the tiniest subatomic particles is made of microscopic strands of energy. This view point can help us understand why energy, sound and vibration are at the frontier of progress in the field of healing. So we can conclude that beyond the deepest level of matter there are vibrational patterns which can be influenced by energy work, sound frequencies and intention. The sound frequencies of HiddenMind obviously resonate on a molecular level as does all music. There is a saying that, "music is heard in the silence between the notes". The effects of music is not just heard, it is also felt. When an affirmation concerned with the heart meridian is used in conjunction with a heart sound frequency from an instrument, the energy of the heart can amplify exponentially and healing of negative emotional states can be experienced.

Sound frequencies are employed to reconnect and carry blue print information to restore the twenty eight cardinal frequencies, deleting the memory of shock and restoring homeostasis to the physical, mental, emotional and spiritual aspects of the person. The subconscious is interrogated through vibrational kinesiology. This involves bio feedback using different types of indicator tools i.e. dowsing (use of a pendulum) or muscle testing and making statements to the subconscious mind, getting vital information about a person's state of health. The subconscious mind will then indicate accurately the exact harmonics to be used for correction. This can also include the spoken word, harmonics from cotton frequencies, scents, and semi-precious stones. Experience has shown that this wellness program has accelerated the healing process for thousands of people who have had bio-energy work and HiddenMind corrections. Sound frequencies can also be used to neutralize viruses and pathogens and again the subconscious mind will indicate which sounds are best to do this.

One of the most amazing features of how sound frequencies work is its ability to influence cells, and pre-cell division to ensure ongoing proper cell functioning of organs and tissues. The human body is made up of over 80% water and there are water crystals along each meridian which carry the frequency or harmonics for the entire length of the meridian, correcting it to its full potential and proper emotional charge. When Tom Griffin studied with the late Cameron Dawson many years ago, he asked him whether such frequencies would work on a child that was born deaf and, amazingly, he responded that they would. This calls into question how we hear. This begs the question as to what our subconscious mind hears that our conscious mind does not?

Sound as metaphor

The metaphorical way that we use words and metaphors in relation to sound is an indication of how we subconsciously know the frequency changes that we can create in ourselves and others. 'I don't like the sound of that', 'this is music to my ears', 'your silence is deafening', 'your words taste like poison', these phrases can induce states of emotion that can be felt in a positive or negative sense. The intonation of a person's voice coupled with intention can have a profound effect on the person being subject to this dialogue. Likewise, healing can be imparted through the voice and intention. The choice of words is also very important here. When a client is listening to the heart meridian affirmation, the sound frequency, the tone of voice, the words or phrases used with intention can alter negative emotional stress patterns, delete shock and instill and lock in an ability that continues to transform negative heart emotional states to a more positive one.

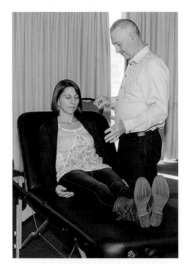

*Tom using his pendulum to ask
questions of the clients
sub-conscious mind.*

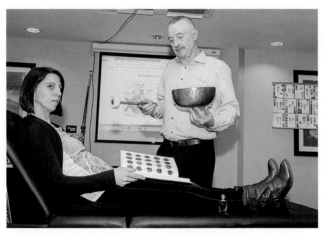

*Tom using chakra bowls and colour frequencies
to make a correction.*

CHAPTER 11

HIDDENMIND

CORRECTION PROGRAM FOR SPECIAL NEEDS

When one or other hemispheres of the brain does not integrate properly this is known as Homolateral Brain Function. This is usually found to be present in all special needs cases. Another consequence of homolateral brain function is hyperactivity in children. The cerebrospinal fluid pulse from the brain to the spine is fourteen pulses per minute in waking mode in a healthy child and twenty eight in sleeping. In a hyperactive child this pulse can be as low as five or six in waking mode and as low as twelve to sixteen in sleep mode. What happens here is that the brain needs nutrients and the body responds to this emergency crisis by pumping in adrenalin, as it breaches the blood brain barrier and quickly replenishes the brain. This unfortunately has the side effect of keeping the child in a hyperactive state and can be responsible for outbursts of irrational behaviour and even rage tantrums.

Rage tantrums are a result of blockages in the Duramater. The cerebrospinal fluid is pumped from the brain between the Dura and the pia mater to the spine all the way down to the sacrum and the sacral pump pushes the fluid back up to the brain. The vertebras of the spine can also show misalignment and may be found not to be in their correct physical position or electrical fields. This can often result in subluxations (interference with a nerve) causing damage to the organs of the body and causing negative feedback between the organs and the spine. When a child is hyperactive, has rage tantrums, difficulty making friends or social skills, neuro developmental problems, sleeping disorders, phobias, fear of being separated from his mother, or is constantly whinging, these are needs that are not being met and the source of these needs need to be addressed.

These symptoms are metaphors; they are reflecting deep subtle underlying faults that need to be corrected. They are indicating that something is wrong and children with such symptoms are looking to the parent/significant other adult to interpret their needs and address them. This unconscious desire by the child to be balanced by the parent is hard wired into the subconscious mind of the child. Unfortunately, parents do not know how to interpret these metaphors and do not realise that they are outwards signs of an inner need. They usually depend on significant others such as psychologists or doctors to diagnose their children and try to address their needs by assigning them to a specific Special Needs category. Medication is often prescribed, for example Ritalin, or in some cases, special needs teachers are assigned to work with these children.

However, this falls far short of addressing the underlying causes of these problems, some of which can be addressed within the HiddenMind corrective programme.

"**Dyslexia**: A learning disorder marked by impairment of the ability to recognise and comprehend written words."[1]

The condition of dyslexia can be corrected by the Hiddenmind Investigative and Corrective Sound Protocol. The correction is achieved by correcting underlying physical and emotional electro-physical disturbances. The correction can be permanent after a number of sessions provided that the original underlying physical and emotional causes remain corrected and in a balanced state. The further causes of learning difficulties will be discussed in detail in the following paragraphs. Dyslexia has no relationship to the basic intelligence of an individual; however, problems arise with observing and transferring information from the brain to the written form as typically seen in the written work of dyslexics with words, figures and sentences often written backwards. Some of the most famous and successful people in history were dyslexic, some seriously so.

The eyesight problems associated with dyslexia are caused by emotional shock which leads to malfunctions of the electrical system causing:

1) Bone structure misalignment of the skull and spine;

2) The left and right brain not reversing the image seen by the eyes causing homolateral brain function (only one side of brain functioning).

The emotional shock which causes dyslexia can be due to birth or pre-birth shock which prevents proper brain integration in later stages of the child's development. However, dyslexia can also occur later in life as a result of emotional or physical shock in a fully integrated child.

Dyslexia can be the cause of a major disability in life leading to illiteracy on one hand or a minor effect leading to tiredness, eyestrain, minor short term memory and minor hearing and cognition problems. This is because the left and right conscious brains are not functioning together naturally. This condition, known as homolateral function, is the opposite of integrated function when the left and right brain are working together without strain. People who have the condition of homolateral function can integrate their brain function but it takes four times the amount of energy to do so. In the case of young children, the subconscious mind will not allow what it regards as an unnecessary loss of energy and refuses to allow the conscious mind the necessary energy to do so as long as the underlying shock is still there. The knock on effect of this is that concentration is retarded and the visual images seen by the eyes are not reversed in the brain - this is called dyslexia.

Males and females have different brain structures and facilities designed to complement their roles in life as males and females. The key differences in the sexes with regard to dyslexia is the size of the corpus callosum which is twenty three per cent less in size in males (Corpus Callosum is the connecting tissue between the left and right cerebra - left and right brains). The hormone testosterone is produced by a pregnant mother in response to her subconscious recognition of having conceived a male foetus. Its function is to convert the inherited shape (initially female) body upon which the cells form to a male body. As well as physical form and genital organ changes in the foetus as it develops, testosterone inhibits the development of the corpus callosum thereby creating male characteristics.

The shortened corpus callosum in males has some advantages over the female brain in relationship to judging spacial distance such as, parking a car, dart throwing, shooting and disciplines that require intense focus such as, chess. The reverse is true with regard to the fact that females have a longer corpus callosum than males, and evidence of this can be seen in their ability to multitask.

Male and female vision differs as a result of the difference in size of the corpus callosum. Females have peripheral vision of 180 degrees or more on average without moving their head. Males have narrowed peripheral vision with an approximate range of between ninety to one hundred and twenty degrees. Females have a wider peripheral vision than males, with the old saying being that women have "eyes in the back of their head". This may be related to the fact that they need multi-tasking abilities in order to watch over young children and keep them safe as they develop. The females extra breadth of vision commences in childhood and allows girls to be able to see two to four letters more than males are able to see at the same age. Males initially have a narrower area of vision than females at the same age. This accounts for the statistical phenomena consistent in all studies relating to children's reading abilities throughout the world, which states that for every female recognised as having a learning difficulty, there are four males in the same statistical group.

In today's society the stereotype roles previously assigned to men and women are reversing or evolving, and women are now involved in areas of work and sports traditionally associated with, and dominated by, men. On the other hand men are now more involved as home carers and house husbands. The evolution of this is leading to individuals having a better balance of male and female characteristics.

Normal Brain Function

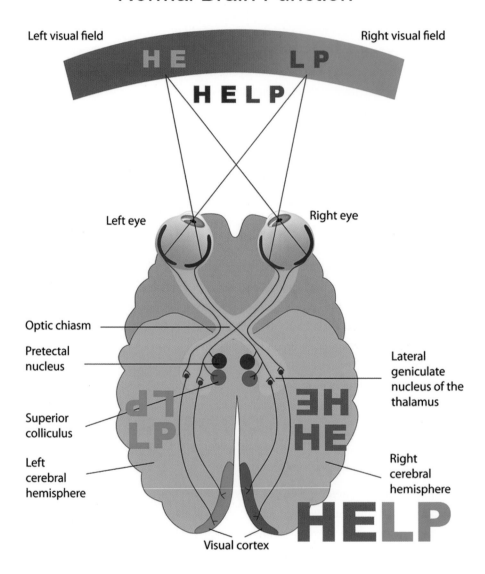

Dyslexic Brain Function

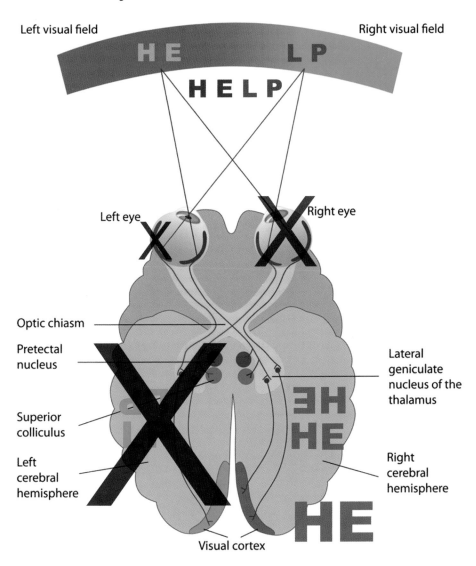

AUTISTIC SPECTRUM

Autism Spectrum Disorder (ASD) is a condition that affects social interaction, communication, interests and behaviour. It includes Asperger syndrome and childhood autism. The main features of ASD typically start to develop in childhood, although the impact of these may not be apparent until there is a significant change in the person's life, such as a change of school.

In the UK, it's estimated that about one in every 100 people has ASD[2]. ASD can cause a wide range of symptoms, which are often grouped into two main categories: problems with social interaction and communication, and restricted and repetitive patterns of thought, interests and physical behaviours. Autism is a developmental disorder that appears in the first three years of life, and affects the brain's normal development of social and communications skills. Autism is the more severe of the ASD spectrum.

ATTENTION DEFICIT DISORDER (ADD)

This condition is diagnosed when a person finds it difficult to retain information. People who have this problem find learning difficult and find their concentration lapses easily. They can get stressed and upset easily, particularly when faced with learning new things. As with dyslexia this can be caused by emotional shock, vaccine damage, environmental shock or all of the above.

ATTENTION DEFICIT HYPERACTIVITY DISORDER (ADHD)

ADHD is more serious than ADD and it is also accompanied by hyperactivity. Children with this problem can get very agitated and are difficult to manage especially at school when they are in a controlled environment. At school they are expected to learn and this can cause them to become more hyperactive and more difficult to control. Sometimes children can get aggressive when confronted and can cause a lot of disruption in a classroom and in the home. Parents can find these children difficult to manage at home as they can be aggressive towards their siblings and often display a lot of emotional and anti-social behaviour patterns. ADHD can be caused by hereditary and environmental factors. Conventional treatments for this disorder are with the use of Ritalin type medications. Diagnosis rates of ADHD have tripled in the past twenty years, while autistic disorder and bi-polar have increased 40 fold[3]. There is a suggestion of over diagnosis of children's mental illness given that the criteria for diagnosis as a mental illness "was plucked out of thin air"[4]. The long terms effects of anti-psychotic drugs on children remain an unknown quantity. The worry is that Ritalin type medications are similar to amphetamines or cocaine, in that they create addictions in young people which may lead to later drug abuse. Also, the impact of labelling ADHD as a mental illness can have a lifelong impact on the young person.

The above conditions are noted on the NHS choices website as "other mental health conditions" for which there is no cure. All of the above disorders can be helped with the HiddenMind investigative and corrective sound program.

For the parents to assist their child's further development they need to change their own energy frequencies. They must realise that they can communicate with the subconscious mind of their child by learning to manipulate their own energies. They need to be able to visualise and see the child in their minds eye as being healthy and happy. They are taught how to communicate with their child in a non-verbal way but with positive intent like they did when the child was in the womb.

During the correction process the child redeems his full programme and his energetic matrix's fully corrects. We teach parents energy techniques in order for them to work with their children at home. We also advise on nutrition as it is a very important feature in the rehabilitation of the child. It is amazing to see how a child who was extremely difficult and insecure on the first day of treatment changes to a calm, independent child even during the four days of treatment.

We would also like to say at this stage that our therapists have great concern for the parents of these children. They are often very stressed out and very worried for the future of their child. They often feel helpless and disappointed in the level of help that they are getting from the institutional health care system. We are also aware that a lot of parents have spent a lot of time and effort getting involved in programmes such as ABA, Speech Therapy, Primal Developmental Therapy, and OT; these can have a beneficial effect on children and can make Tom's work more effective and more easily applied.

CHAPTER 12

POST CORRECTION CHALLENGES

Tom speaking from his Clinic

One of the most challenging features of the corrections carried out during the HiddenMind Program is how to educate the parents to deal with reactions in children after the first correction. These reactions can be from mild to severe, but are not seen in every case. However, in some cases they are part of the healing process and there is a great need to explain to the parents of these children what is actually going on. Usually the reactions that challenge the parents greatly are the intensity and a worsening of the original presenting symptoms.

I have seen this many times in my clinic when some parents contact me after treatment, to say that their children's symptoms have periodically presented themselves. I will ask the parents to return to the clinic in order to check the child over and reassure them. It is also necessary to check that all the corrections have held and have not been undermined in any way. If all the corrections are still in place, then I explain that there is a transfer of new information happening from the subconscious to the conscious mind, because the child's full programming is returning.

Initially symptoms and/ or extreme behavioural patterns can get periodically worse but these usually calm and balance themselves out over a period of time. As the brain is reintegrating and as the energetic matrix becomes fully charged, the behaviour patterns can improve and the child will begin to behave in a more balanced way. In the cases of severally hyperactive children suffering with ADHD this can be very challenging for the parents. If the child is younger he may be managed easily, but if he is a teenager his behaviour may be more challenging.

The good news is that positive changes are also observed in between these scenarios which gives the parents the resilience and hope to continue with the programme until such problems are resolved or improved. It is explained to the parents during the first correction that it can take from six months up to a year, with at least three to four corrections, plus bio-energy work and nutrition before the child will feel the full benefits of the therapy. It is also necessary to educate the parents with regards to how best to support the child and each other whilst these changes are taking place.

There are other factors which can also undermine or interfere with the child's correction. For instance, if a child gets a virus or a bacterial infection, this can undermine the healing process or it can freeze the programme while the body is dealing with these pathogens. In the event of this happening, the child will usually need another special correction to clear the pathogens and to move forward with their healing process. Environmental problems such as Geopathic (Earth) Stress can also effect children as well as adults causing a type of shock, which can also be identified and corrected by the HiddenMind programme. However, if relevant, there is much published information available on the subject of Geopathic stress, but to explain it in any more detail is beyond the remit of this book.

If a child experiences a shock from an emotional, physical or environmental trauma, this can undermine the correction. Children who have been corrected can experience negative thought forms and negative emotions from other people or other children which can subliminally affect the corrections and these will need to be cleared by a practitioner. This is why a series of corrections over a year is of great importance.

After the second correction, people are advised to use a patient corrective sound CD in order to help with the changes post correction. This is sometimes also used after the first correction. The CD contains a series of sound frequencies which are advised to be used on a weekly basis to assist the patient's healing. I also advise families that a family correction may be necessary because there are connections between each member of the family that is unique to that family. For example, a full correction was carried out on a child of ten years old to correct for Learning Difficulties. During this HiddenMind programme, I corrected malfunctions in the child's meridian, chakras and auric fields. Her hemispheres were not connected nine months after birth, causing only one side of the brain hemispheres to be working correctly.

The child had also had hereditary problems affecting her in her first trimester affecting her meridians on one side; three of her cranial bones were out of alignment on one side with the temporal, parietal, and sphenoid bones fixated and not articulating. Her atlas and her cervical vertebrae were also misaligned resulting in her cerebrospinal fluid pulse being totally deficient, resulting in excessive adrenaline being pumped into the brain causing hyperactivity and anxiety. Her facial bones on one side were also out of alignment. One leg was measurably shorter than the other due to the malfunction of the kidney meridian, which was all due in this case to a trauma with the birthing process. The child was also found to have been adversely affected by the side effect of vaccines, as well as by anxiety states and thought forms. A full correction was carried out which was followed by four days of bio energy work. The mother was given advice regarding nutrition to support the corrections and was asked to bring the child back to the clinic within a time period of six weeks. A month later the mother contacted me and said her daughter had improved immensely for four weeks but suddenly started showing some of the original symptoms. She was quite worried so I asked her to bring the child back for a consultation.

When I checked the subconscious mind of the child, there was an indication that she had been affected by a thought form from another member of the family. This caused emotional shock and undermined the original correction. I identified that she had been affected by a negative thought form via a relation (whom I identified) on her mother's side of the family. I asked the mother if she could identify with this in regard to the person mentioned. She said she wasn't surprised as the relative in question never dealt with anything and always dumped negative emotions on other people. Most of what I had corrected in the child the month before had become unbalanced and as a result some of the original symptoms started to re-emerge.

As soon as I released the negative emotion in question through the HiddenMind Programme, the child felt an immediate release. The mother could see the changes in the child; her colour became more natural, her leg length re-adjusted in balance with the other leg and her eyes came back into focus. She had previously had a strabismus (squint). The mother asked for an explanation as to how this could happen.

I explained that as the child was the first one in the family have a correction, the subconscious mind of the relative picked up on this and transferred unexpressed thought forms and negative emotions to the child in the hope that they would be released through the child. This is a phenomenon that has fascinated me over the years. When a child or other member of a family receive a correction they unconsciously sometimes act as a conduit for releasing the meridian malfunctions, or negative thought forms of other family members.

According to Cameron Dawson, founder of the Dawson Program on which the Hiddenmind Programme is based, the child in the womb is subconsciously communicating with every member of the family tree for a number of generations of the past, a number of generations of the future and a number of generations laterally. Certain members of family and extended family, brothers, sisters, aunts, uncles, even cousins can be bouncing negative emotions, anxiety states, thought forms, belief systems off each other often causing conflict or tensions between those individuals. This may explain why tension between two brothers or families can remain unresolved down through the generations. This is why when subconscious thought forms are released, other family members with unresolved issues, can unconsciously pick up on the correction taking place and again unconsciously home in on what is taking place in order to resolve their own hereditary and acquired issues.

This is not to be feared. It is commonly accepted that negative and positive characteristics are passed on from generation to generation. It happens all the time in families and this is why if a child needs a correction, it is advisable for the whole immediate family to have a correction as well as the one child. If we take a simple metaphor such as "like father like son" or "a chip off the old block" or "the apple doesn't fall too far from the tree". These descriptive metaphors suggest a genetic link in terms of inherited personality characteristics which are passed on throughout the generations, indicating that there was always some awareness of family links in past history.

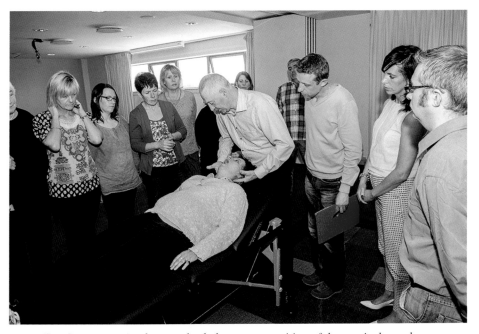

Tom Demonstrating how to check the correct position of the cervical vertabrae.

CHAPTER 13

SYMPTOMS AS METAPHORS

LOWER BACK PAIN AND SPINAL PROBLEMS

Tom Griffin, in his clinic over the last twenty five years, has dealt with many clients with lower back pain and a number of other back and spinal problems ranging from mild to very severe. When clients come to the clinic for healing they often have exhausted a range of both orthodox and alternative treatments. Most people who come for treatment have had no previous experience of energy work and it is always explained to them that energy healing is a necessary complement to other therapies in order for holistic healing to take place.

Some clients are very informed with regard to diagnoses from their medical consultants and, in particular, from their orthopaedic surgeons. They are also knowledgeable about the results of investigations such as X-rays, MRI and Pet Scans. However, many people who attend Tom's clinics have already gone down these roads but are not happy with the outcome. In some cases, initial relief was experienced but has proved to be short lived. Others have gone on to experience new symptoms in addition to those they first presented.

Tom explains to his clients that the basis of his treatment is energy manipulation. This is based on the fact that the human body is composed of energy and that there is an invisible field of energy surrounding and permeating the physical body. If this energy becomes blocked or stagnant through emotional shock or physical trauma, the immune system becomes compromised and pain and disease can manifest. The structural anomalies, slipped or prolapsed discs, chronic inflammation, and nerve pain can sometimes be caused by unresolved or underlying rage or anger. It may well be that the person is unaware of this, as it may be stored away in the subconscious mind. In the case of the former, this can sometimes result in the brain depriving the muscles and nerves of blood and oxygen, causing severe pain and inflammation. This in turn will cause the meridians to become overloaded with negative emotional charges causing them to shorten. This will inevitably cause physical distortion in the vertebrae which will affect the intervertebral discs, causing inflammation in the muscles.

If the brain initiates this process it is with a view to distracting the conscious mind in order to protect it against the effects of underlying dangerous negative emotions, which at a conscious level the person is unable to deal with without emotional support.

In his book, *"The Divided Mind"*, Dr. Sarno, an expert in psychosomatic disorders, states that a large percentage of musculoskeletal symptoms are psychogenic in nature in that they are emotionally induced and are usually the result of unresolved and repressed emotions. The basic premise of the neurophysiology of psychogenic disorders is that emotional states are capable of inducing physical symptoms with or without the physical alteration of specific tissues in the body. He refers to symptom such as, lower back pain, upper shoulder pain, migraine, irritable bowel syndrome, peripheral neuropathy, fibromyalgia, prolapsed discs, nerve and muscle inflammation, as being psychosomatic in origin provided there is no medical evidence of physical/ structural defects. However, it is important to note that these symptoms and pain are not imaginary; but because western medicine does not recognise their emotional causation they have become public health problems.

The definition 'psychosomatic' is a much bandied around term and has acquired a very bad press due to the prejudice in society towards the term. Dr Sarno suggests that unconsciously we would rather have physical pain than acknowledge any kind of emotional turmoil. What western medicine doesn't recognise is the very strong connection between the brain and the body also known as the body-mind experience. For instance, it is recognised that there are experiences in the form of events or traumas that cause us to have strong emotional reactions which are neurologically branded by the brain and bring about chemical changes in our bodies. The term psychosomatic in the context of this chapter means that the brain has created these conditions as a distraction to the conscious mind to prevent it from experiencing the intensity of dangerous emotions, or other traumatic experiences buried deep within the unconscious mind.

The HiddenMind programme seeks to correct the physical, mental, and emotional aspects of the person by first identifying the underlying causes. For instance, the investigative protocol can identify precisely when and why rage occurred, and/or can highlight all the features associated with an emotional or physical trauma. This procedure can dilute the intensity of the memory to a point where the conscious mind can accept the much diluted memory without being consciously traumatised. It is at this point that the brain lets go of the need to create distractions and the proper mind-body relationship can manifest. The relaxation response of being pain free is truly empowering, allowing the person to experience a sense of balance, confidence and control.

M.E. Myalgic Encephalomyelitis

Over the past number of years an alarming number of young women in their late teens and early twenties have presented suffering from post-viral syndrome, ME and fertility problems. They range right across the spectrum from [delete as too Irish-centric] students to professional people, teachers, nurses, bank officials and career women with ages ranging from seventeen to early thirties. One such client who presented at the clinic was a professional who hadn't worked for over a year, had very little energy and was housebound during this period of time. Her mother, who was aware of the hidden-mind protocol, brought her to the clinic in the hope that she could be helped. Her presenting symptoms and diagnosis was that of M.E. – Myalgic (muscle pain) Encephalomyelitis (inflammation of the brain and spinal cord).

ME is described by the Irish ME Trust as a complex and debilitating physiological illness involving neurological and endocrinal dysfunction and immune system dysregulation. There is no improvement with bed rest and symptoms can worsen with physical or mental exertion. Other related symptoms may include fever, sore throats, painful irritability, poor concentration and sleep dysfunction. Many ME sufferers will pinpoint a viral infection as the start of their illness, although no particular virus is present in all cases. One theory related to the condition is that the breakdown in the body's defence mechanism allows a viral infection to occur more easily. It is known that approximately 12,000 people suffer from ME in Ireland alone. It is interesting to note that if six or more of the cardinal frequencies are not functioning, the subconscious mind may allow a virus to take root in order to slow a person down in order to conserve their energy.

The protocol used in the treatment of M.E. is: Bio-energy therapy, together with the unique Investigative and Corrective Sound HiddenMind Protocol, which dramatically boosts the immune system. From past experience, clients often have additional symptoms such as chronic fatigue, depression, anxiety, irritable bowel syndrome, fertility problems and an inability to be creative or to look forward to the future. It may be that there are much deeper causes than a virus or emotional stress or work overload at play here. Experience with clients tells us that the root cause may lie as far back as early childhood or even as far back as to the time in the mother's womb. Within the treatment protocol we have a unique way of accessing such information both in relation to their early childhood and to pre-birth.

Many females, although treated medically, are still suffering from post-viral symptoms months and even years later. These symptoms can present as, chronic tiredness, depression, anxiety, severe menstrual problems etc. It is only when the cardinal frequencies and the cranio-sacral pulse are restored that the subconscious mind allows the brain to fully reintegrate.

This is usually followed by an emotional release and often flu-like symptoms, during treatment or immediately afterwards. Further treatment sessions using Bio-energy and corrective sound frequencies are usually advised and these set the stage for a full recovery and the person can begin their journey back to health.

DEPRESSION

People who present at my clinic with symptoms of depression, usually have had it for some time. Some have been on medication for years but their depression has never fully dissipated to their satisfaction and they cannot get off medication for any length of time without reverting back to full depression mode. When we look at the typical symptoms of depression they are usually associated with feelings of helplessness, lack of self-belief, low energy and vitality. Other symptoms can present such as, the inability to look forward to the future, feelings of being a burden on friends and family and in extreme cases an overwhelming compulsion to end it all. This is mainly due to not being able to find appropriate resolutions to their dilemma, in this three dimensional reality. People who suffer from depression may also have problems sleeping.

The standard medical approach to treating depression is via pharmaceutical medication. Sometimes psychotherapy is advised but usually not enough to deal with the condition. The conventional medical approach is to correct low serotonin by use of anti-depressant pills thus increasing the happy hormone, the lack of which is associated with the condition. While this approach can benefit people they are usually only recommended for short term use.

Often people have tried to take their own lives or have done themselves serious personal harm by the time they present themselves at my clinic. Before agreeing to take them on as clients, they are instructed that they must keep in regular contact with their doctor or psychiatrist for constant evaluation of their medication. It is the policy of our organisation not ever to advise or encourage clients to stop taking prescribed medication.

The "Hidden Mind" approach to depression is first and foremost a holistic one. It looks initially for blockages in the energy system and encompasses bio-energy as part of the treatment in order to balance the energy fields. However, it also looks at and deals with, the causative factors associated with depression through exploring the subconscious with the hidden-mind protocol, and deals appropriately by correcting what is highlighted. For instance, In the case of depression, the first features for which a correction is carried out are to correct the three electrical systems, namely the chakras, meridians and auric fields. As discussed previously, these three electrical systems make up the 28 cardinal frequencies which are the energetic blueprint or template for our physical being.

The seven chakras enter the body at specific sites, including the brow, throat, heart, solar plexus and hara (lower abdomen). The chakras connect the life force energy and give vital information through the meridians to all systems of the body including the brain, heart, and all major organs. They also connect to the three nervous systems, the kundalini (first auric field), the meridian and the endocrine system. The chakras should have a 100% positive emotional charge but in the case of depression, this can be as low as 20% leaving 80% of the chakras with negative emotional energies. It is very important to remove the sick emotional energy and to balance the chakras. This procedure is initiated by Bio-energy Therapy prior to corrections.

The next energetic features to be balanced are the meridians. The meridians are pathways of energy that vibrate eclectically throughout the human body and which also supply all the organs and chakras with vital life force energy. Meridians flow is one continuous movement around the body like an electrical grid. They cannot be seen with the naked eye. However, their existence has been scientifically verified using special equipment (see scientific proof, need ref to earlier chapter/s). All illnesses whether mental, emotional, physical or environmental are associated with partially or fully blocked meridians. Meridians can be corrected with Bio-energy, kinesiology and the Hidden Mind techniques.

The auric fields are the other seven cardinal frequencies which are of extreme importance when treating depression. They act as powerful antennas drawing in energy, information vibrations and impressions from the world around us. The outside layers connect us to our bloodline, our environment and can connect us to any family members at any distance. They also act as filter systems for this information in order for us to process it. If the auric fields are depleted or have a low energy frequency, health can be negatively affected. For instance, if our auric fields are functioning at about 20% of their normal capacity, negative thought forms, negative emotions or anxiety states from other people cannot be filtered out and can clog up our emotional and energetic systems.

This is usually experienced as over-sensitivity, uneasiness when in the company of other people or an overwhelming sense of fear and anxiety when in confrontational situations. As a result people often withdraw into themselves and try to avoid any communication with other people and the world around them. Low auric field frequency can also be responsible for repetitious negative thought patterns and negative mind-set with regard to emotional scenarios. Other causative factors of depression can be associated with hereditary or bloodline faults going back to the birthing experience again. If these faults are not cleared from our energetic blue prints they can be a big factor in a depressed person's condition. These faults can be sourced back generations and often clients can relate to this as they can recognise traits emanating from parents, grandparents and extended families.

Another important feature to check when treating depression is brain integration. The hemispheres of the brain can become separated with shock or stress overload. This causes the stress hormones to become over excited as the cranial bones tighten, and more adrenalin needs to be pumped into the brain. Over time this can result in adrenal fatigue and burn out if not corrected and can also cause low serotonin. If serotonin is low it cannot make sufficient amount of melatonin which is responsible for sleep, resulting in sleeplessness and insomnia. When serotonin is low there is usually not enough cerebral spinal fluid created to pump through the spine at the correct frequency. The cerebral spinal fluid frequency should be an average of fourteen pulses in waking mode and twenty eight during sleep. In some people who are depressed, the pulse can be as low as four or five in waking and fourteen to eighteen in sleeping. The brain needs nutrients and the enteric nervous system (also known as the second brain) pumps adrenaline to compensate. In times of stress or emergency this can give an extra boost of energy but if the hemispheres of the brain are not integrated correctly and the cranial bones are tightened or fixated, confusion and lack of concentration can be experienced.

When these faults are identified and neutralised by the HiddenMind protocol using special meridian affirmations, together with the chakra and auric field corrective balancing frequencies, the immediate feeling of lightness and joy is expressed by so many people.

What is outlined here are some of the features that the HiddenMind protocol takes into consideration when dealing with depression. There may be other factors to consider as well such as the depressed person's occupation, bullying at work, having confidence shattered by superiors or co-workers, boredom or lack of interest or feeling trapped at work. Or on the other hand, there may also be adrenal burn out from being a workaholic. Problems within the family can also drain a person's energy. All of the above can be contributory factors in depression.

Another very serious area to consider is suicide. People can be affected by the suicide of a relative or a friend or even someone unknown to them in their area. The energetic debris left behind when people commit suicide can have an overwhelming negative affect on people. This residual energy can often be a catalyst in causing other people's energy systems to overload or break down, resulting in suicide or depression. The Hiddenmind protocol can detect these influences and reverse their negative effects on people. When these causative features have been addressed and corrected this can re-empower people in a very positive way.

ANXIETY

Severe or chronic anxiety has to be one of the most debilitating illnesses for a client to have to deal with. It can affect people at any time in their lives. It can be associated with chronic stress and shock. Within the clinic environment, many people present with symptoms of anxiety ranging from middle to severe. Even mild anxiety can cause people not to be able to deal with the challenges of everyday living. In a number of cases this condition has been a lifelong experience.

Severe anxiety can drain your energy and activate your stress hormones to unacceptable levels. This can present a situation where your body is full of cortisone, epinephrine, and noradrenalin, the flight, fright and fear hormones. Chronic anxiety can also be associated with panic attacks. People in this state find it very difficult to stay focused and can be uneasy. While medication and lifestyle changes can help, the HiddenMind Protocol looks deeper for causative factors such as family matters, grieving and personal loss. People who have phobias and OCDs can experience huge anxiety when presented with situations that trigger them. People have presented to Tom's clinic who said they never had any great worries or health problems and suddenly have developed severe bouts of anxiety. This becomes very frightening for them and they often find it difficult to pin point any cause. It is Tom's experience that anxiety is always associated with cranial bone fixation which always warrants further investigation through the "HiddenMind programme".

In the HiddenMind programme the emphasis is on re-empowering the client by imparting to them tools and techniques to enable them to take back responsibility for their own health. For instance, clients are advised about the importance of diet and nutrition. They are also taught relaxation, meditation and emotional transformation techniques and how to use a self-corrective sound system to enable them to take control of their own healing.

HiddenMind Corrections: A brief Summary

To treat a client holistically there are many corrective modalities to be dealt with. The hemispheres of the brain must be reintegrated, cranial bones need to articulate or pulse correctly, cranio-sacral fluid pulse must be at the correct frequency. The electrical integrity of the spinal column must be re-established by correcting the three electrical systems (the meridians, chakras and auric fields). In addition, the electrical integrity of the spine can be affected by negative energy thought patterns from another person or place of abode which must also be cleared through the HiddenMind programme. Taking back control for one's health is advised after treatment. This can be through active meditation techniques, breathing exercises and internal focus to turn stress into vitality. Lifestyle changes are also discussed, especially when the lifestyle has contributed to the condition or illness. Nutrition and diet are also factors that need to be considered. There are foods and supplements that are serotonin enhancing and mood enhancing. Proper nutrition is part of holistic wellbeing.

The objective of the HiddenMind and Bio-energy combined programme is to restore the mind-body relationship by deleting pain and inflammation in order to allow the body to return to optimum health. A series of sessions is advised for people with chronic or severe problems. These usually consist of three (four day) bio-energy sessions, approximating forty five minutes per sessions. During these sessions the hidden features or causes of the presenting problem are investigated through the Hidden-mind protocol. The investigative protocol consists of healing sound frequencies, meridian affirmations, bio-energy techniques, and many more techniques which have been discussed throughout this book. Such frequencies were used for centuries in many ancient cultures to correct the physical structure of the body, to connect the unconscious to the conscious mind and to restore health and vitality to the human being.

While this therapy may seem very esoteric, energy based and alternative, Tom bases the structure of his therapy on anecdotal evidence (testimonies), previous research and twenty seven, years of experience.

The work of Tom and his colleagues has given hope to hundreds of people who have come to his clinic seeking help when all other medical avenues have been exhausted.

The evidence of the power of the HiddenMind and Bio-energy combined program is supported by the many clients who have experienced a return to good health as well as a realisation that they are not passive observers in the game of life, but rather keepers of the realm of their own health and well-being.

The testimonials that Tom has received from his clients are too numerous to include in this book. However, a subset have been included in the appendix.

CHAPTER 14

Men's Health – The mid-life Experience

Tom Griffin

A Compassionate View from a Fellow Traveller

When writing about men's health it is difficult to paraphrase or be inspired by any major research, because little has been written on this subject in recent times. We see the odd statistics and alarm raised in the media concerning the startling rise in male suicide and how professional bodies and self-help groups are called upon to offer some sort of answers and solutions to a growing problem. So this article on men's health is based on personal experiences and the experiences of male colleagues and friends who are involved with the HiddenMind programme. It is about an aspect of men's health that is often ignored by our society at large and by men themselves possibly because it is out of sync with societal expectations of male behaviour. It relates to the late middle age period of a man's life sometimes referred to as the 'man-o-pause'.

Much has been written about the female menopause and most men would have an idea of what women go through and the associated side effects as literature on this subject is readily available. One only has to look at the magazine racks in any shop to notice how hard it is to find a book on men's health, and where they may exist, they do not cover the men's issues I have to confront in my clinic every day.

My reflections are mostly about middle aged men and, as I am one myself, I have first-hand experience. When men come to me for help they are looking for someone who can help them to move on in their life. Someone who can create a shift in their thinking, a shift in their consciousness, improve their energy, as they find it very difficult to motivate themselves, to help themselves deal with anger, grief, lack of self-confidence or more serious issues such as depression or even with suicidal tendencies. Often these men go down the road of anti-depressants and/or psychotherapy, and indeed some men have benefited from these. However, when they present at my clinic, they are looking for something more and it is that 'something more' that I wish to discuss here.

Let us take a typical scenario where a forty seven year-old man says that, "every day is becoming a huge challenge". When he gets up in the morning he does not have any energy or enthusiasm, there is nothing in his life that gives him any joy or kick anymore. He is a professional person with twenty five or more years of work behind him; he is married with children, has worked hard to put them through third level education or career choice; he has worked very hard to be the best he could be as

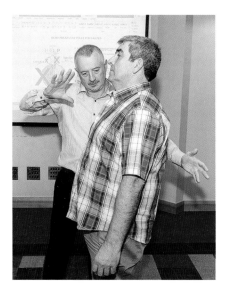

A Bio-Energy Demonsration

father, husband and provider. But now that he is getting older, his energy is nowhere near what it used to be and his physical health is starting to show serious implications, from high blood pressure to arthritic conditions. These are things he could cope with if he had the mental energy and peace of mind instead of the growing fear and anxiety he feels for the future.

He is confused and full of guilt because his wife and children love him; he is financially ok but senses that this is not enough. He knows that he has to find within himself the answers to his own dilemmas. This is why he can suddenly appear awkward or conflicting and can often hurt the ones he loves. He may be drinking too much alcohol or gambling to trying to forget how low he feels, but the reality hits him always afterwards. How can I help this man?

Firstly I explain that he has never experienced being middle aged before and that at this stage men need to reassess their lives, their goals, their ambitions for the future, their values and self-worth. They many need to rediscover how to love and allow them-selves to be loved. They may need to let go of some of their hardened attitudes towards their masculinity and learn to transform negative patterns of emotional stress.

Such a person needs to become aware of the energy blockages which may be associated with certain traumatic experiences in his life. He needs to become aware that his energy has been misdirected by ignoring the right side of his brain, the feminine side, which is not to be confused with being over feminine. This feminine or right brain energy is associated with self-reflection, emotional transformation, spiritual awareness, cyclical thinking as opposed to linear thinking. The feminine side involves accessing the creative side, not just for creating tools and computers but for a continuous redefining and reshaping of his own attitudes.

In order that he can have a say in his future, he has to change his consciousness. He needs to realise that he is the co-creator of that future. Therefore he has to take control of his life and to realise the power of his own creativity. He needs to live in the present moment.

As HiddenMind practitioners, we have at our disposal many tools and techniques with which to redirect his energy, in order to restore balance between the left and right hemispheres, the male and female sides. This will contribute to unlocking the hidden potential that he contains. This is why he needs to access the feminine aspect of his being, as it contains an inexhaustible source of light energy. In accessing the feminine side he is enabled to re-absorb this energy into his daily life and alter his thinking and his attitudes in a positive way. He is more affected by his environment than he realises. The constant negativity regarding the recession, the rise of unemployment and the negativity we are exposed to in our media system, can lead him to feel insignificant and powerless. This is why he needs to move inward, to find the spark of light, to open the gateways to the higher vibrations. Reading this article on men's health may help to encourage you the reader to make the choice to be healthy, happy, have purpose in your life and have a connection to an abundant source of energy in your life for our wellbeing and mental health.

Epilogue by Tom Griffin

Co-writing this book has been a personal journey of reconnection for me. My extensive experience in healing and the subtle energy world has helped me to see a bigger picture of reality. I can now see that every experience or challenge has many strands attached to it and inbuilt in these experiences is its own solution. I now understand that I have to think with my heart with compassion to understand consciousness and the true nature of reality. This book is written at a time in history when scientists, particularly quantum physicists, are talking about consciousness as a way to understand the "bigger picture" or "the nature of reality".

Quantum physicists say that we are all holograms of this bigger reality and by virtue of this we are all connected to the source of everything and we cannot be separate from it. Quantum physics tells us that there are unlimited expressions of this bigger reality and unlimited possibilities, allowing us to co-create our existence and our future. All reality is connected through a unified field and this creates the possibility for us to connect to other dimensions and other aspects of our own being. Gregg Braden, scientist and philosopher, says in the "Divine Matrix" that compassion from the heart is necessary to understand this concept and he also talks about the power that each one of us has to positively affect our own lives and the lives of other in the past, present and future. Quantum physics tell us that consciousness creates matter, not vice versa as postulated by the mechanistic view of science. Science is one language to explain the universe, philosophy is another. Compassion and love are also the language to understand the universe.

During the course of writing this book I had the opportunity to visit South Africa. During this visit I visited Capetown. Particularly memorable was my visit to Robben Island where Nelson Mandela was incarcerated for 18 of his 28 years in prison. I always had a great admiration for Nelson Mandela, like many people throughout the world, and was touched, humbled and inspired by his ability to forgive everyone who tortured and imprisoned him.

When I heard a talk by an ex-prisoner who was imprisoned with Nelson Mandela, describing the conditions of their imprisonment, the intensity of emotion and compassion I felt was overwhelming and brought tears to my eyes. Other people in the group felt the same. I watched other men in the group like myself trying to hold back the tears. I was feeling tremendous compassion for those prisoners and I questioned how men could be so cruel to their fellow human beings.

Then I remembered something Nelson Mandela said after he was released that struck me like a revelation. He said:

"Do not recognise me for my achievements but for all the times I got up after falling down."

At that moment I realised what the Quantum physicists were talking about when they say we are all connected to an invisible field where past, present and future interconnect. I felt at that moment that the love and compassion manifested by myself and all the other people there, and indeed millions of other people like me that stood on that island, were not separate from the inspiring energy Mandela felt when he got up after falling down. The rational mind may find it hard to comprehend that the inspiration that Mandela felt, and the compassion and love that was felt at this moment in time, are simultaneous realities and that his spirit in the transcendent world is the same spirit we are all part of, connected by the field. He showed the world through forgiveness that all human suffering can be transcended and that forgiveness and compassion can bring people together in a more powerful way than by any violent means. I also realise what quantum physicists mean when they say that when you change a particle at a moment in time, it changes in the past and in the future. Standing in Mandela's cell has affected my future thinking in that every conflict has its conclusion built into it and that compassion, forgiveness and love can create a bridge to wholeness and peace.

Another example of the unified field is synchronicity. I had one particular experience two years ago which I found to be extraordinary. This happened while I was travelling to Australia accompanied by members of my family. We had three days in Dubai, in the Arab Emirates, as I always wanted to visit there. As anyone that has visited that part of the world knows, alcohol is not readily available in restaurants, and pubs are only situated in hotels or compounds. On the last night of our stay at 11.30pm, accompanied by my son I eventually located a bar not far from where we were staying. When I had ordered two beers I heard an Irish voice behind us say, "no matter where you go in the world, you will find an Irish man". We introduced ourselves to this stranger and he introduced himself to us and it transpired that he was a fellow Mayo man who had moved to Dubai with his family six years previously. During the course of the conversation he informed us that he and his family lived in Abu Dhabi, about 150 miles away, and that they had come to Dubai to see a specialist as they had a very sick child and were desperately trying to find out what was wrong with her so that something could be done to help her.

My heart went out to him and I informed him that I treat a lot of sick children and had a special protocol to work with children in the Autistic Spectrum Disorder category. He said that his wife was very worried about their daughter but that she had great faith in the angels that her daughter would eventually be helped. I informed him that I was flying to Australia the next day at 2pm but that I would check his child and treat her with the HiddenMind protocol in his hotel the next morning if he and his wife were open to it. My son Andrew and I arrived at his hotel at 10am. We met the rest of his family; he had two children, a boy and a girl called Aishling and she was their great concern. She was eight years old and she looked pale and out of sorts. Her mother told me that she was so weak she could not climb the stairs on her own. She informed me that they were in Dubai to see yet another specialist to see if her child could be helped and cured. I took out my pendulum and started to question her subconscious mind to get a deeper understanding of why she was so ill. I discovered that she had suffered birth shock, which her mother confirmed, and the consequences of that was lack of brain integration which hindered her neurological development and was a catalyst for a whole lot of other health problems which were now manifesting. I picked up a lot of information in relation to her electrical systems and biological functions. I did a correction on her using special healing sounds. I informed the parents that I did a subtle energetic correction and this would start a healing process for her. I informed the parents that I would be in Australia a month and I would continue to do distance healing on her on a weekly basis. Each week her mother texted me and during that time each of the specialists she consulted came up with a number of diagnosis and diseases. One specialist mentioned that she had Epstein Barr syndrome. Another diagnosed irritable bowel and low thyroid function. I told her to have patience and keep me informed on her progress. However these specialists could not prescribe any treatment for her at this point as she was an enigma to them.

Three week after her correction in Dubai, her mother texted me to report that her daughter had started to improve and that the family would come to Ireland at Christmas and they would visit my clinic. She asked me if I would continue to treat her at a distance before that and I agreed. I saw her daughter in my clinic after Christmas 2014 and she was much improved. I treated her with Bio-energy, and HiddenMind investigative & corrective sound protocol and informed her mother that it could take her another few weeks to fully benefit from the treatment. She also started using the patient maintenance CD that contained a series of sounds and frequencies to assist her healing on a daily basis. Two months later, Aishling's mother rang me from Abu Dhabi and said her daughter was doing exceptionally well. The only way I can explain this story is through the new view of connected consciousness, involving the unified field which connects people's thoughts and emotions.

Aishling's mother, through her faith and belief in asking a higher power to help her sick daughter, sent a signal to the field of consciousness which through an extraordinary synchronized way connected me to her on my way to Australia. She took the obvious safe route by attending reputable doctors and specialists but the real answer to her daughter's problems was not going to be found in a drug or capsule but in an extraordinary meeting with the founder of the HiddenMind protocol. Meeting her father that night in the pub in Dubai was the point of real change in his daughter's condition. The unified field is the medium in which everything is connected in the universe which transcends space and time. Aishling's return to health was a quantum possibility, a reality which potentially already existed on some level of her being. The compassion and love felt by her mother manifested this reality for her child. I was only the bridge. Through my knowledge and experience of working in the subtle energy world and the subconscious mind, I created a bridge to her true potential by restoring her energy system and neural pathways to experience balance and homeostasis in this three dimensional reality.

It is interesting to note that there is a biological centre in the brain that can greatly help us to communicate with the transcendent or spiritual realms. This centre is known as the pineal gland. This gland has been symbolised by a number of religious and esoteric literature as a pine cone, as this mirrors the physical structure of the gland. The pine cone in esoteric literature is associated with the brow or the third eye chakra. The pineal gland becomes awakened at night through the interaction of melatonin and DMT which is created naturally in the body. This gland is responsible for dreaming and out of body experience when we sleep. Esoteric literature says that this gland allows us become aware of the spirit world and other realms. Perhaps this might explain why answers often come to light in the morning after having gone to bed with seemingly un-solvable problems. During sleep the pineal gland can help us access information about the solution to a dilemma which may not be available to us in the waking state. When it says in the bible "let thine eye be single" it is referring to the pineal gland or third eye, indicating its ability to access truth beyond the ability of the rational mind. When the head, which contains an active pineal gland, and the heart through compassion and love, work together as one, this creates a powerful bridge to manifest quantum possibilities and experiences in this reality. Gregg Braden states that in his visits to Tibet he had become aware that all the books of all religions, including the missing books from the Christian bible, were recorded and secretly stored there. He found a saying in the book of Thomas that he found interesting: "when two people in the one house become as one you can tell the mountain to move and it will move". In other words, when the pineal gland and compassion work as one, anything is possible. Braden was fascinated that the monks were chanting continuously and not asking for anything specific. He asked the head monk about this and the monk told him that they believed that they already had what they wanted and the chanting helped to create the feeling or compassion which was the bridge. The head monk said that if you had to ask for something from the divine that you are already disconnected. This showed that the pineal gland and the heart working together was the key to manifestation.

Another fascinating feature of the Hiddenmind protocol is the ability to detect negative hereditary features downloaded to people in the womb and afterwards. A patient I was treating in my clinic four years ago stands out in my mind. Anne (alias) attended my clinic in Claremorris, Co Mayo because she heard about me through my internet site and she said she had a strong feeling that I could help her. She also brought her four-year old son for treatment. She informed me that she was thirty-three years old and she was suffering from anorexia, was chronically depressed and seriously anxious. She said her mind was in a constant state of negative thinking and she even had suicidal thoughts. She said that she had been attending top physicians in London but was not getting any better. She informed me that her son had learning difficulties and ADD. At the end of the 1st session I informed Anne that 85% of all her negative thoughts were downloaded from her bloodline and she had not accumulated this in her life time. She looked amazed and awestruck. I told her that she had been carrying this with her all her life and it had never been identified and processed. I informed her which of her parent's bloodline it came from and how many generations it went back, and the number of electrical systems that were negatively affected. She said that this was a new and wonderful revelation to her and asked what I could do about it. I informed her that once I had identified all the relevant information I could clear it with the corrective sound protocol, which I did. I also asked her subconscious mind to give me an idea of how many pounds weight all this negativity represented. The answer I got is that it would be equivalent to thirteen pounds weight. She informed me that she always felt that she need to lose a stone (fourteen lbs) hence her anorexia and now she realised that it was not a stone in weight she needed to loose but the negative downloads I had identified. I treated Anne and her son for four days with Bio-energy and the HiddenMind investigative & corrective sound protocol and told her that I would like to see her in six weeks' time.

Anne's symptoms were metaphors mirroring unresolved emotional debris buried deep in her subconscious mind and unidentifiable?? by orthodox psychiatry. One month later Anne contacted me and said that she was feeling much better and had gained a stone in weight; she told me that she was an artist and when her health deteriorated she had not been able to pursue this career any more.

She invited me to come to England to treat herself, her family and her friends which I did some weeks later. After the second treatment she was feeling extremely well and had once again started to pursue her career in Art. Her mother told me that during that time that they had taken their daughter to numerous physicians in London but were getting nowhere. She said, "My daughter went over to Ireland to your clinic and she came back a different girl".

My experience of working with Anne showed me that no matter how sick or down that people are there is a latent potential for wholeness and wellbeing which can be manifested through interaction at a subtle energy level and also through compassion.

Testimonials

In April 2013, our son Daniel (19) came down with a sudden illness and after it was investigated in the A & E in hospital it was established to be a severe viral condition which affects joints, stomach giving off a red rash.

Although he received excellent care from the A & E and our GP, the fact that his illness was viral based, meant it had to run its course.

We had come across the Hidden Mind while attending Bio Energy and were aware of the great results achieved by a Hidden Mind Corrective Sound treatment, so we made an appointment with Tom Griffin.

When we arrived for the treatment, Tom assessed the severity of his condition, and established that a Hidden Mind treatment would benefit Daniel, and proceeded to give the treatment with Bio Energy and Corrective Sounds.

To our amazement Tom was able to pin point exactly what was attacking the system, where it was in his body and how it would be treated. Tom and two others began to work on Daniel by giving him Bio Energy and Tom then proceeded to give him a Corrective Sound treatment. An hour later we left, agreeing to attend for another treatment within 3 days.

On the way to the clinic, Daniel was unable to hold a conversation due to the discomfort of travelling. On the way home, he was able to hold a conversation and asked for something to eat. This was a massive turnaround as he hadn't wanted food for days.

Tom was able to tell us that he had 46 viruses attacking his system. The Corrective Sound treatment was able to kill these viruses which resulted within a week of up to a pint and a half of purple fluid being released from the rashes which had developed into what looked like swollen blisters. We got a corrective sound CD from Tom which Daniel had to listen to in order to allow these sounds get his body to continue healing itself.

I can honestly say that from the moment Tom began the treatment, Daniel stopped getting worse and started his journey to recovery. Daniel received two subsequent treatments from Tom and over a 3 week period made significant improvements. He also began to put back on some weight. Within 4 weeks he was able to sit college exams.

This was an amazing turnaround for Daniel. We are truly grateful for the work and interest Tom took in Daniel's case and the healing that followed.

E. O'D.

Testimonials

I suffered from sciatica last September as a result of a trip from a vehicle. I regarded it as an accident. I went to my GP as I was in severe pain; originating in my right buttock/hip and travelling down my right leg. My ankle was the most painful and the toes on my right foot were numb.

I went for an MRI scan and was found to have disc degeneration at L4, L5 and S1. There was pressure from these discs protruding onto the nerve roots of both L5 and S1. The pain was severe.

I was given top end pain relief medication both orally and by injection. I couldn't sit, stand or walk. I spent most of my days lying on the living room floor. The medication would barely take the "sting" out of the pain but nothing was killing it. I lost two stone in weight from the pain over a 10 week period. The GP's advice was to wait for a period of 8 weeks and then their plan was to have me seen by a back specialist.

I didn't want to have such medical interference as a suggestion of an operation was mentioned and I was afraid that my back would never recover from such a procedure.

At approximately 10 weeks into my diagnosis; my partner brought me to visit Tom Griffin. He used a combination of Hidden Mind therapy and Bio Energy therapy on me. Within twenty minutes of being treated by Tom; the numbness left my toes for the first time in 10 weeks! The pain considerably reduced to a manageable level. He diagnosed the exact problem without any equipment!

I went home delighted with the results. I was able to reduce the pain relief medication almost immediately. I saw Tom in total three times and made a complete recovery.

The GP is amazed as according to her reading of the MRI Scan; I shouldn't be able to stand let alone be fully recovered! It is an amazing therapy that Tom uses and teaches and I highly recommend anybody with health issues to consult with him.

C. Mac C.

Testimonials

I had to write to you and tell you how greatful I am for all your help. I still find it hard to believe how bad or sick I really was, and how I put up with my pain for so long.

To say I knew nothing about Bioenergy is putting it mildly, I had heard about Tom a few times from different people but still hadn't heard in detail what, or how Bioenergy worked or helped people. I had been going to the doctor for years with the same problems, chronic stomach pains, absolutely no energy, blood rushes, dizzy spells, no appetite, irritated, hair loss, the list goes on. I had a lot of scopes and medical investigations but I wasn't getting any definite results which was very upsetting and frustrating as I felt so bad and knew something was wrong. I was starting to feel like a broken record. I felt like the doctors weren't taking me seriously, and I was starting to get really worried they were missing something, but I felt my hands were tied and I couldn't go to the doctors again.

My family were getting very worried about me as they saw a big change in me and that I wasn't my usual bubbly self. A friend of mine mentioned Tom and the Bioenergy to me again and I said I was going to give it a try.

I was slighty sceptical at my first appointment, Tom didn't ask me my problems at first, he hovered over me with his hands for a while and what happened next amazed me; he started to tell me what I was feeling and why I was feeling that way.

He described how I was feeling and some of my symptoms, and explained it was because of a blockage in my gut. He told me he could definitely help me, and the rest is history.

I left that day with a huge feeling of relief, and after three days of treatment I began a new lease of life. Of course you're not cured on the first day but over the weeks and months that followed, I starting getting back to myself, my energy levels were back and my life was back on track.

Again when I look back I can't believe how sick I was and thanks to Tom and his family I am totally back to normal.

I urge anyone to try Bioenergy, and not just as a last resort, I fully intend on having a few more treatments throughout the year if I feel I need a boost.

Thank you so much Tom and all the very best to you all for the future!!!

Aisling

32 Years old

Testimonials

I have had concerns for quite a while about my daughter, she was looking very sickly for at least a year and her demeanour and behaviour had disimproved, firstly I put it down to teenage years but after seeing Avril I figured out it was a lot more complex than we realised. After the first treatment I could see a change in her behaviour and her confidence grew. I could see a major improvement in both her behaviour and her self-confidence she was much happier in herself. Unfortunately we had a set back as she needed surgery.

After surgery she developed a strange facial twitch and was irritated and embarrassed by same. I immediately contacted Avril and we arranged a session and Avril's correction rectified the problem and also uncovered some personal emotions which were affecting her health. We were astounded by Avril's capabilities to uncover and rectify these issues. Through her correction she could give details of the exact time events happened that had consequences on her health and behaviourism's.

Avril has a wonderful way of communicating with people, my daughter was very comfortable in her company. Avril has a wonderful aura about her and has me as a parent totally at ease and very confident in her abilities anytime we have associated with her. I would highly recommend Avril and the hidden mind programme.

D.D.

We as a family attended Avril for a course of treatment. We were open to alternative treatments as we had heard wonderful reports of their work.

Our three sons are all feeling the benefits of Avril's treatment; our eldest had a pain in his back and post treatment is feeling much, and feels he has a lot more energy and is better able to deal with the demands of college. The others are also reaping the rewards of sleeping better, less anxious and more energy. We are also feeling much better and more energetic than previously.

We would really recommend Tom and Avril as their care and attention was second to none; their professionalism and management of each and every one of us was sincere and very individually centred. We thank them for their help to each and every one of us.

N.S.

Testimonials

I began bioenergy in April 2014 after a major open abdominal surgery. I had tried acupuncture, reiki and physiotherapy previously and while I found some effect, I wasn't keen to continue. My first session with Avril in Claremorris was interesting. It was like nothing I'd seen before. I learned a lot about myself with the Hidden Mind and found the crystal bed intriguing. I listened to the affirmations and sounds and after some initial giggles, I felt very relaxed.

Afterwards, I felt like a weight was lifted from my weary shoulders. I was far less anxious and the post-op depression I'd been suffering with had improved massively. I took away methods that I could put in to use in my everyday life and I love returning for top-up sessions.

In May 2008 I had my first little girl by Emergency C-Section. I contracted MRSA on my blood cultures from theatre. In 2010 I was diagnosed with Type 1 diabetes and I am insulin dependant since. In May 2013 I had my second little girl by planned C-Section because of previous history and me being a diabetic.

Since I had my first baby in 2008 I battled with extreme fatigue which just getting progressively worse. When I mentioned this at regular routine hospital appointments I was told I was a diabetic and a busy Mom and no wonder I was tired! I also suffered from extremely heavy periods.

Early Summer 2014 I started experiencing shortness of breath. As the summer went on it got worse and in October I decided to revisit my GP as now I was also experiencing pains in my chest and occasional sharp darts to my heart/ chest area. All regular blood tests were done and returned normal. A stress test in November was normal. I was at a loss as to what was happening to me but I knew I couldn't go on this way.

A friend of mine recommended that I rang Tom Griffin, which I did and I started the 4 day course on Monday 8th of December. On that day Tom did some bio-energy to cleanse the body. He also did a cranial correction as he said the cranial bones hadn't fused correctly and this would have attributed to my bad health.

On the following 3 days I was treated by Avril Griffin. Avril cleared energy from me which I was carrying from both my Grandmother and from another young woman who had died in my locality.

She informed me that I had received a bite in my left leg and that was what was causing the stabbing pain in my chest. She cleared this together with 5 other viruses from my system.

Testimonials

Avril found that I had retained 25% of my youngest daughter's energy from birth. She subsequently passed that energy back to Cara and the result of this was unbelievable. Cara had been extremely demanding of me since the day she was born. Now she is a happy go lucky independent little girl who potters off to play and entertain herself even when I am in her company.

Cara also required some correction of her cranial bones. Her immune system was also quite low and has been improved by attending Avril. She also had viruses in her system which have been eradicated.

As there had been a lot of tragedy in my husband's family following on from the death of his 3 brothers at a young age there was a lot of energy which needed to be cleared in order for our health to improve.

Since attending the Clinic just a few weeks ago I feel so much better. I feel as though a weight has been lifted. I have so much more energy. I have no pain and I am starting to get my life back. I now realise that as a result of numerous shocks to my system over the years my immune system was compromised. I also understand now the importance of the Cranial Bones fusing correctly as this can affect the rest of ones life.

I am grateful to both Tom and Avril for what they have done for my family. They welcomed me into their Clinic in their house and treated me without any invasive procedures or drugs for ailments that the medical profession were unable to pin point not alone treat.

C. G.

My name is Noel H.

Three years ago I developed Crohns disease. I had followed the medical route in search of relief but to no avail. In fact, the opposite occurred. I was getting worse with the medication I was taking. Eventually, and thankfully, I heard of Tom Griffin and his bio-energy through a friend. At this stage I could hardly digest the slightest bit of food and had dropped below seven stone in weight. I booked an appointment with Tom and the rest is history. From the first clinic I noticed a difference. The bloated stomach was gone and my appetite returned and I haven't looked back. Since then I was hooked. I had to learn more about this magical wonder. I completed a kinesiology course and recently qualified as a Bio-energy Therapist. – Something I couldn't have imagined three years ago. Thesis the new Medicine.

Testimonials

Our daughter Faith was born in May 2010. Faith was a very agitated baby, showed digestive problems, was very hyperactive and attended an ophthalmologist because she had a turn in her left eye and kept walking into things. Faith contacted the chicken pox virus in October 2012 and subsequent to this she started having seizures at intervals of 10 days. Faith was diagnosed with Temporal Lobe Epilepsy (TLE) in November 2012. Since November 2012 Faith has been subjected to many different anticonvulsants in order to control her seizures but unfortunately Faiths seizure frequency increased, her behaviour became extremely difficult, she was extremely fatigued all the time, poor eyesight, interaction with her peers was poor and her immune system was extremely low causing her to contract any infection/virus quite easily. Faith has been seen by three neurologists and three ophthalmologists in three different countries.

Faith was seen by Tom Griffin the 1st week of September 2014, since her first session of therapy we have not looked back. After the first day with Tom Griffin on the Monday, Faith sat at the kitchen table and had a very lucid conversation with me this had not happened before and she looked me in the eye while we spoke; Faith prior to this session with Tom was no longer making eye contact.

Faith has been attending Tom Griffin and Avril Griffin since for treatment. Both Tom and Avril are fantastic with Faith, Faith loves going to see them and she seems to be very interested in the bio energy herself, she keeps asking for Martina Griffin to do work on her, work is what Faith refers to as the bio energy so I know she is getting relief from it. Faiths behaviour has improved dramatically she is not as hyper, she has not had an antibiotic since Tom Griffins intervention, I do not have any concern with her eyesight she has stopped running into things and she is making eye contact, Faith is sleeping much better she is not as fatigued and Faiths seizure frequency has spaced out. Faith looks well and she has a quality of life again as have we all.

Faith is still attending Tom and Avril Griffin for ongoing treatment.

I came to Tom Griffin twenty five years ago for Bio-energy treatment with Tom. I had an ulcerated stomach and was in terrible pain and was taking eighteen tablets a day.

After the first four days I felt a little worse for a few weeks. I gathered up the courage to return for another clinic and after that I got complete relief. I have never taken a tablet for my stomach since. I would recommend bi-energy treatment to anyone

C. O.

Testimonials

I have been going to Tom Griffin's Bio-energy for twenty four years, the reason being that I got results from it. The first time I went I had a bad knee with pain and I couldn't bend it. I had four days of treatment. I didn't tell what was wrong as I wanted to see if anything would happen. After the third day I got an aching all around my two hips and down the one foot where I had the bad knee. The next morning it was gone but there was a tingling under the toes of the bad knee. When I went back on the fourth day of treatment Tom asked me if there was any movement. I told him my story and he said 'good, we have things moving. They sure were. I went back again the next month of treatment and it never gave me any trouble for the past 22 years. Then it came back in the summer of 2012. It was even worse than before and I couldn't do my walks or my gardening. I went back again for more treatment. By Christmas 2012 I was back again in full flight. No pain or ache so there can be no doubt there. I have never taken any pain relief or any other medication. I don't believe in them. I am 71 years old and the energy I have I owe to the Bio-energy.

M. McL.

Our daughter Heather was nearly four years old when diagnosed with Asperger's Syndrome. This started our journey that brought us in contact with Tom Griffin. Asperger's syndrome is a conditioning where people can be high functioning but have difficulties with social skills, emotions and it is on the autism spectrum. We were told that early intervention was required and benefits are best seen if acted upon prior to age seven, when the brain is fully formed. Along the way we met very helpful people across various fields. We engaged with speech therapists, occupational therapists, to early intervention services of the HSE.

We were quite distressed as various reports and assessments indicated Heather had several difficulties. Heather did not score well in various areas including speech, social concepts, balance etc. At one point we had to walk away from HSE as they indicated Heather would not fit into mainstream school.

On our quest for help we engaged with various therapies such as, listening therapy and Plexus bio-energy. While attending the Plexus bio-energy the healer Derek suggested we meet Tom Griffin, a person he worked with. As Heather's father, I must admit, I was sceptical at first but was open minded and willing to see what benefits Tom could bring. My wife Helen was the driving force in making this decision. Like any parent you would do anything in your power to help your children.

Meeting Tom for the first time was an experience I will never forget. Heather was totally relaxed and what Tom discussed with us made sense. It tallied with what other professionals said. The only difference was that all the other therapies tinkered at the edges without dealing with the root causes. Follow up sessions involved his son and daughter doing the treatments. As a father, I was stunned and impressed at by their passion and willingness to help others. Tom's work has transformed our daughter Heather. She is in mainstream school performing very well; she is very sociable with lots of friends and is doing ballet. Ironically, our biggest difficulty is getting the school to see she needs less and less interventions and fulltime in class is the best option going forward. I guess they are not used to parents looking for less support after a journey like ours. We see out daughter Heather, now 7 is no longer a girl with aspergers with barriers in the way, but a girl with the world at her feet.

As Heather's father I have been won over by Tom's work and I am currently attending him for help on some ailments I have been suffering from.

M. H. & Heather. April 2012.

My Testimonial

I brought my three year old son Aidan to Tom's clinic in Galway in February of this year. Aidan had a very severe divergent squint, which had been operated on twice to try to rectify, unsuccessfully. Tom began working on Aiden, and within a few minutes of connecting to Aiden's energy system Tom was able to tell me that Aidan's cranial plates had not fused after birth, which I now know ae vital to the functioning of the brain. Tom was also able to tell me that the fall I had encountered while carrying Aiden in my fourth month of pregnancy had a very significant part to play in his brain function. With the caesarean section delivery and vaccines after birth, all of these were contributing to the cause of the divergent squint. Tom began with the correction and Aiden listened to the Tibetan sounds. Within a few minutes I could see that Aiden's eye began to move into alignment. I was truly astonished at what I had learned and what I saw. Following the correction, Aiden began to do more than he had previously been able to. He began to ride a bike and was far more physically confidant than he had been. I feel this was due to the fact that his brain was now functioning correctly for the first time since he was born. I have no doubt that Aiden had a severe learning difficulty that now, thanks to Tom, has been rectified. Following two more corrections with Tom, and a perfect pair of eyes, I brought Aiden back to the eye specialist in Dublin who carried out the two operations. She kept looking at her notes and then at Aiden's eyes and was clearly unable to fathom what had happened to him, as the two operations had not been successful. Myself and Aiden are eternally grateful to Tom and his abilities. Thank you! Xxxxxx

J. F.

Testimonials

This is a thank you to Tom Griffin Bio-energy healing. I can honestly say that Tom was responsible for getting my Son back to good health. When John was three months old he suffered from chest infections, wheezing caused by viral respiratory infection. He was on antibiotics, injections and in hospital on many different occasions. When he would get an attack, he would be gasping for breath. We had many sleepless nights.

When Tom started in Irish….. Co Mayo, twenty five years ago I took John down to his clinic. We met Tom and he started to treat him. He had six or seven sessions of Bio-energy healing. We could see the improvement every week. After the last session Tom told me John might get worse to get better. After a few weeks, John got a very bad attack, but thank God, he never looked back since. Again a big 'thank you' to Tom and also his wife Martina. You have the gift of healing. I would have no hesitation in recommending Bio-energy healing.

Mary - A grateful Mother.

I am now a retired Secondary School Teacher. I often meet former students and love to talk to them about their progress through life. On one of those occasions while shopping in Dublin I met such a person in Tom Griffin. We were delighted to meet each other. We talked about our schools and school mates and school colleagues. I knew that Tom was making a name for himself in an unusual area at the time. He was treating people through a unique Bio-energy method to overcome various problems. I told him that I had such a problem and challenged him to find and cure this ailment. He gave me a thorough examination and found that one of my toes was injured and had gone septic. He worked on it with his great Bio-energy process and on two more occasions in his clinic. The toe is cured and never gave me any trouble ever since. Thank you Tom Griffin and that you may continue to heal anyone who comes to you with a problem.

END NOTES

CHAPTER ONE

1   Wren Barbara. Cellular Awakening. How you body holds and creates Light. Hay House. London. 2009.

2   Dieppe Paul: Limitations of Empirical Science in Conventional Medicine & CAM balens 2nd CPD Conference, May 2013.

3   Wren Barbara. Cellular Awakening. How you body holds and creates Light. Hay House. London. 2009.

4   IBID

5   Braden Gregg. The Divine Matrix. Bridging Time, Space, Miracles and Belief. Hay House Inc, USA. 2007.

6   Pawluk,Dr. http://drpawluk.com/education

7   DeVries Jan. Body Energy. Mainstream Publishing. 1992

8   Eden Donna with Feinstein David, PhD. Energy Medicine for Women. Aligning Your Body's Energies to Boost Your Health and Vitality. Penguin Group (USA) Inc New York. 2008.

9   McTaggart L. The Field , Harper Collins 2001

10 Myss Caroline, PhD. Why People Don't Heal and How They Can. A practical Programme for Healing Body, Mind and Spirit. Bantam Books. UK. 1998.

CHAPTER TWO

1   Davies Paul. The Goldilocks Enigma. Why is the Universe Just Right for Life? Penguin Books. London. 2007.

2   Braden Gregg. The Divine Matrix. Bridging Time, Space, Miracles and Belief. Hay House Inc, USA. 2007.

3   IBID

4   Gersh-Nesic, Beth. www.about.com

5   Young Thomas. Cited in Paul Davies. The Goldilocks Enigma p275. 2007.

6   Wren Barbara. Cellular Awakening. How you body holds and creates Light. Hay House. London. 2009

7   DeVries Jan. Treating Body, Mind & Soul. Alternative Solutions for

END NOTES

Modern Living. Main stream Publishing. Edinburgh. 2003.

8 IBID

CHAPTER THREE

1 Rubik Beverley: The Journal of Alternative & Complimentary Medicine.
   Dec 2002, 8 (6): 703-717. doi:10.1089/10755530260511711.
   published in vol 8 issue 6: July 5, 2004.

2 Pawluk,Dr. http://drpawluk.com/education

3 Berger Hans. Caton Richard: Neurol Neurosurg Psychiatry. 74(1);9. Jan 2003

4 HeartMath (1991) cited in Braden. www.HeartMath.com/company/index.html.

5 Rubik Beverley: The Journal of Alternative & Complimentary Medicine.
   Dec 2002, 8 (6): 703-717. doi:10.1089/10755530260511711.
   published in vol 8 issue 6: July 5, 2004.

6 Lipton Bruce H. PhD. The Biology of Belief. Unleashing the Power of
   Consciousness, Matters and Miracles. 7th edition. Hay House Inc. USA. 2009

7 Hunt Valerie V. Infinite Mind. Science of the Human Vibrations of
   Consciousness. Malibu Publishing. California 90265. 1996.

8 Rubik Beverley: The Journal of Alternative & Complimentary Medicine.
   Dec 2002, 8 (6): 703-717. doi:10.1089/10755530260511711.
   published in vol 8 issue 6: July 5, 2004.

9 Burr Harold Saxton. Blueprint for immortality. London: Neville Spearman, 1972.

10 Becker, R. The Body Electric: New York: William Morrow. 1998.

11 John Muir, cited in Rubik, Beverley: 1994. Measurement of the Human Biofield
   and other energetic Instruments. In Ch 20 of 'Energenetics and Spritualiy'.
   Lyn Freeman.

12 Hunt Valerie V. Infinite Mind. Science of the Human Vibrations of
   Consciousness. Malibu Publishing. California 90265. 1996.

13 DeVries Jan. Treating Body, Mind & Soul. Alternative Solutions for
   Modern Living. Main stream Publishing. Edinburgh. 2003.

END NOTES

CHAPTER FOUR

1   Samantha-Laughton Dr. M. The Genius Groove. The New Science of Creativity. Paradigm Revolution Publishing. UK. 2009.

2   Woolam C. www.canceractive/epigenetics.com

3   Lipton Bruce H. PhD. The Biology of Belief. Unleashing the Power of Consciousness, Matters and Miracles. 7th edition. Hay House Inc. USA. 2009

4   Eden Donna with Feinstein David, PhD. Energy Medicine for Women. Aligning Your Body's Energies to Boost Your Health and Vitality. Penguin Group (USA) Inc New York. 2008.

5   Lipton Bruce H. PhD. The Biology of Belief. Unleashing the Power of Consciousness, Matters and Miracles. 7th edition. Hay House Inc. USA. 2009

6   Lipton Bruce H. PhD. The Biology of Belief. Unleashing the Power of Consciousness, Matters and Miracles. 7th edition. Hay House Inc. USA. 2009

7   Eden Donna with Feinstein David, PhD. Energy Medicine for Women. Aligning Your Body's Energies to Boost Your Health and Vitality. Penguin Group (USA) Inc New York. 2008.

8   Lipton Bruce H. PhD. The Biology of Belief. Unleashing the Power of Consciousness, Matters and Miracles. 7th edition. Hay House Inc. USA. 2009

9   Radin Dean. The Conscious Universe. Harper One. Barnes Noble. 1997.

10 Braden Gregg. The Divine Matrix. Bridging Time, Space, Miracles and Belief. Hay House Inc, USA. 2007.

CHAPTER FIVE

1   Hunt Valerie V. Infinite Mind. Science of the Human Vibrations of Consciousness. Malibu Publishing. California 90265. 1996.

2   Chopra Deepak. The Book of Secrets. Rider, London. 2004.

3   Hunt Valerie V. Infinite Mind. Science of the Human Vibrations of Consciousness. Malibu Publishing. California 90265. 1996.

4   Grandy, John K. The Neurogenetic Correlates of Consciousness.

5   Narby, J. Cosmic Serpent: DNA and the Origins of Knowledge. London: Phoenix 1999.

END NOTES

6   Samantha-Laughton Dr. M. The Genius Groove. The New Science of Creativity. Paradigm Revolution Publishing. UK. 2009.

7   IBID

8   Garajajev, Dr. Pjotr. (Gariaev Peter) & Poponin Vladimir. DNA BioComputer Reprogramming; http://www.psychicchildren.co.uk/4-3-RussianDNAResearch.html

9   Monarch Butterflies - Source - National Geographic Website.

10 Goswami, A. The Self-Aware Universe. Tarcher/Putnam. Cited in Lawton: Genius Grove. 1985.

CHAPTER SIX

1   Myss Caroline, PhD. Why People Don't Heal and How They Can. A practical Programme for Healing Body, Mind and Spirit. Bantam Books. UK. 1998.

2   IBID

3   IBID

4   Lipton Bruce H. PhD. The Biology of Belief. Unleashing the Power of Consciousness, Matters and Miracles. 7th edition. Hay House Inc. USA. 2009

5   Frankel R.M.. Quill T.E. and McDaniel S.H. 2003. The Biopsychosocial Approach: Past, Present, Future. Rochester NY. The University of Rochester Press

6   Soukup, Alisha R. The Mind-Body Narrative: The evolution of Psychoneuroimmunology and its implications for Nursing Research and Practice St. Catherine University. Sophia. March 30, 2012.

    A student project in partial fulfilment of the requirements of the Honours program

7   Eden Donna with Feinstein David, PhD. Energy Medicine for Women. Aligning Your Body's Energies to Boost Your Health and Vitality. Penguin Group (USA) Inc New York. 2008.

8   Soukup, Alisha R. The Mind-Body Narrative: The evolution of Psychoneuroimmunology and its implications for Nursing Research and Practice St. Catherine University. Sophia. March 30, 2012.

    A student project in partial fulfilment of the requirements of the Honours program.

END NOTES

9   Eden Donna with Feinstein David, PhD. Energy Medicine for Women. Aligning Your Body's Energies to Boost Your Health and Vitality. Penguin Group (USA) Inc New York. 2008.

10 Britten, Nicky. Medicines and Society. Patients, Professionals and the Dominance of Pharmaceuticals. Palgrave Macmillan. 2008.

11 Lipton Bruce H. PhD. The Biology of Belief. Unleashing the Power of Consciousness, Matters and Miracles. 7th edition. Hay House Inc. USA. 2009

12 De Vries Jan. Treating Body, Mind & Soul. Alternative Solutions for Modern Living. Main stream Publishing. Edinburgh. 2003.

13 IBID

14 Waitzkin, H. The Politics of Medical Encounters: How Patients and Doctors deal with Social problems. New Haven, CT: Yale University Press. 1991

15 Britten, Nicky. Medicines and Society. Patients, Professionals and the Dominance of Pharmaceuticals. Palgrave Macmillan. 2008.

16 Bent N. A. Tennant, T. Swift, J. Posnett, P. Scuffham, M.A. Chamberlain. Team Approach versus ad hoc Health Services for Young Adults with Physical Disabilities: a retrospective Cohort Study. The Lancet. October. Vol 360. P1280-1286. 2002.

17 Dieppe, Prof. Paul: Limitations of Empirical Science in Conventional Medicine and CAM. Balens 2nd CPD Conference 2013.

18 Lipton Bruce H. PhD. The Biology of Belief. Unleashing the Power of Consciousness, Matters and Miracles. 7th edition. Hay House Inc. USA. 2009

19 Davidson Richard J. PhD, with Begley Sharon. The Emotional Life of your Brain. How to change the way you Think, Feel & Live. Hodder & Stoughton. London. 2012.

20 Pert Candace B. Ph.D. Molecules of Emotion. Why you feel the way you feel. Cox & Wyman, Reading Berkshire. 1997.

21 Prendergast J. The Uncommon Doctor: Dr Joe's RX for Managing Your Health. Canada 2006

22 Hunt Valerie V. Infinite Mind. Science of the Human Vibrations of

END NOTES

Consciousness. Malibu Publishing. California 90265. 1996.

23 Mitchell Edgar D. Institute of Noetic Sciences.
    http://www.noetic.org/person/edgar-mitchell/

24 Kelly, Dr. John. Stop Feeding Your Cancer. One Doctor's Journey.
    Penthiam Press. Dublin. 2014.

25 Day Philip. Web Article. Cancer Things I Have Learned:
    A Cautionary Tale: Campaign For Truth In Medicines. credence.org

CHAPTER SEVEN

1   Myss Caroline, PhD. Why People Don't Heal and How They Can. A practical
    Programme for Healing Body, Mind and Spirit. Bantam Books. UK. 1998.

2   Rossi Ernest L. The Psychobiology of Mind-Body Healing: New Concepts of
    Therapeutic Hypnosis. WW Norton & Co. Inc. New York. 2nd Ed 1994.

3   Zubieta Jon-Kar et al. Placebo Effects Mediated by Endogenous Opioid Activity.
    Journal of Neurosciences. 2005

4   Crum, A.J. & Langer, E.J. Mind-set Matters. Exercise and the Placebo Effect.
    Psychological Science,18, 165-171. 2007

5   Boultron Isabelle et al. Placebos Without Deception: a Randomised Control
    Trial in Irritable Bowel Syndrome. PLoS ONE, 5 (12). Dec 2010

6   Dispenza Dr. Joe. You are the Placebo. Making your Mind Matter.
    Hay House. London. 2014.

7   Myss Caroline, PhD. Why People Don't Heal and How They Can. A practical
    Programme for Healing Body, Mind and Spirit. Bantam Books. UK. 1998.

8   Pert Candace B. Phd. Molecules of Emotion. Why you feel the way you feel.
    Cox & Wyman, Reading Berkshire. 1997.

9   Dispenza Dr. Joe. You are the Placebo. Making your Mind Matter.
    Hay House. London. 2014.

10 Kirsch Irving & Sapirstein Guy. Listening to Prozac but hearing Placebo:
    a Meta-analysis of Anti-depressant Medication. Prevention and Treating.
    Vol 1 June. 1998

11 IBID

END NOTES

12 Golomb Beatrice A. M.D., Ph.D. et al. research and Reporting Methods. Anals of Internal Medicine. 153(8):532-535. 2010.

13 Weil Andrew M.D. Spontaneous Healing. How to Discover and Enhance your Body's Natural Ability to Maintain and Heal Itself. Little Brown and Company. London 1995.

14 Pert Candace B. Phd. Molecules of Emotion. Why you feel the way you feel. Cox & Wyman, Reading Berkshire. 1997.

15 Cousins Norman. Forward in 1st Edition of Ernest L. Rossi. 1986.

16 Dispenza Dr. Joe. You are the Placebo. Making your Mind Matter. Hay House. London. 2014.

17 IBID

18 Lipton Bruce H. PhD. The Biology of Belief. Unleashing the Power of Consciousness, Matters and Miracles. 7th edition. Hay House Inc. USA. 2009

19 Pert Candace B. Phd. Molecules of Emotion. Why you feel the way you feel. Cox & Wyman, Reading Berkshire. 1997.

20 Kaplan G.A. Camancho T. Perceived Health and Mortality: A nine year follow up of the Human Population Cohort. Am J 1983 Mar; 117 (3) 292-304

21 Britten, Nicky. Medicines and Society. Patients, Professionals and the Dominance of Pharmaceuticals. Palgrave Macmillan. 2008.

22 Radin Dean. The PSI Taboo in Action. IONS. 2010. www.noetic.org

23 Dieppe, Prof, Paul: Limitations of Empirical Science in Conventional Medicine and CAM. Balens 2nd CPD Conference 2013.

CHAPTER EIGHT

1   Hunt Valerie V. Infinite Mind. Science of the Human Vibrations of Consciousness. Malibu Publishing. California 90265. 1996.

2   Dougans Inge. Reflexology. The Five Elements and their Twelve Meridians. A Unique Approach. Thorsons. Wales. 2005.

3   Eden Donna with Feinstein David, PhD. Energy Medicine for Women. Aligning Your Body's Energies to Boost Your Health and Vitality. Penguin Group (USA) Inc New York. 2008.

END NOTES

4   Lipton Bruce H. PhD. The Biology of Belief. Unleashing the Power of Consciousness, Matters and Miracles. 7th edition. Hay House Inc. USA. 2009

5   Dougans Inge. Reflexology. The Five Elements and their Twelve Meridians. A Unique Approach. Thorsons. Wales. 2005.

6   IBID

CHAPTER ELEVEN

1   www.Wikipedia.org.

2   NHS Website, UK.

3   Dr Allen Frances. Interview by John Nash. Children who are wrongly labelled mentally ill. Daily Mail. July 2013.

4   IBID.

BIBLIOGRAPHY

Baggot Andy. Foreword, Barbara Wren. Cellular Awakening. How your body holds and creates Light. Hay House. London. 2009

Bent N. A. Tennant, T. Swift, J. Posnett, P. Scuffham, M.A. Chamberlain. Team Approach versus ad hoc Health Services for Young Adults with Physical Disabilities: a retrospective Cohort Study. The Lancet. October. Vol 360. P1280-1286. 2002.

Boultron Isabelle et al. Placebos Without Deception: a Randomised Control Trial in Irritable Bowel Syndrome. PLoS ONE, 5 (12). Dec 2010

Braden Gregg. The Divine Matrix. Bridging Time, Space, Miracles and Belief. Hay House Inc, USA. 2007.

Britten, Nicky. Medicines and Society. Patients, Professionals and the Dominance of Pharmaceuticals. Palgrave Macmillan. 2008

Chopra Deepak. Reinventing The Body, Resurrecting The Soul. Rider, UK 2010.

Chopra Deepak. The Book of Secrets. Rider, London. 2004.

Chopra Deepak. Tanzi R.E. Super Brain. Unleash the Explosive Power of Your Mind. 2013.

Conrad Peter. The Medicalization of Society: On the Transformation of Human Conditions into Treatable Disorders. 2007.

Cousins Norman. Forward in 1st Edition of Ernest L. Rossi. 1986.

Crum, A.J. & Langer, E.J. Mind-set Matters. Exercise and the Placebo Effect. Psychological Science,18, 165-171. 2007

Davidson Richard J. PhD, with Begley Sharon. The Emotional Life of your Brain. How to change the way you Think, Feel & Live. Hodder & Stoughton. London. 2012.

Davies Paul. The Golidlocks Enigma. Why is the Universe Just Right for Life? Penguin Books. London. 2007.

Day Philip. Web Article. Cancer Things I Have Learned: A Cautionary Tale: Campaign For Truth In Medicines. credence.org

De Vries Jan. Inner Harmony. Achieving Physical, Mental and Emotional Well Being. Main stream Publishing. Edinburgh & London. Reprinted 2001.

De Vries Jan. Treating Body, Mind & Soul. Alternative Solutions for Modern Living. Main stream Publishing. Edinburgh. 2003.

De Vries Jan. Body Energy. Mainstream Publishing. 1992

Dispenza Dr. Joe. You are the Placebo. Making your Mind Matter. Hay House. London. 2014.

Dougans Inge. Reflexology. The Five Elements and their Twelve Meridians. A Unique Approach. Thorsons. Wales. 2005.

Dyslexia: Source: Webster's Revised Unabridged Dictionary.

Eden Donna with Feinstein David, PhD. Energy Medicine for Women. Aligning Your Body's Energies to Boost Your Health and Vitality. Penguin Group (USA) Inc New York. 2008.

Engle, George L. The Clinical Application of the Biopsychosocial model. Am J Psychiatry: 137:535-544. 1980.

Hanson Rick. Hardwiring Happiness. The practical science of reshaping your brain - and your life. 2013

Hunt Valerie V. Infinite Mind. Science of the Human Vibrations of Consciousness. Malibu Publishing. California 90265. 1996.

BIBLIOGRAPHY

Idler, E.L. Benyamini Y. Self-rated Health and Mortality: A review of Twenty-studies. Health and Social Behaviour 38. 1997: 21-37.

Kamm Laura A. Intuitive Wellness. Using Your Body's Inner Wisdom to Heal. 2007.

Kaplan G.A. Camancho T. Perceived Health and Mortality: A nine year follow up of the Human Population Cohort. Am J 1983 Mar; 117 (3) 292-304

Kirsch Irving & Sapirstein Guy. Listening to Prozac but hearing Placebo: a Meta-analysis of Anti-depressant Medication. Prevention and Treating. Vol 1 June. 1998

Lipton Bruce H. PhD. The Biology of Belief. Unleashing the Power of Consciousness, Matters and Miracles. 7th edition. Hay House Inc. USA. 2009

McTaggart L. The Field, Harper Collins 2001

Myss Caroline, PhD. Why People Don't Heal and How They Can. A practical Programme for Healing Body, Mind and Spirit. Bantam Books. UK. 1998.

O'Doherty M. & Griffin T. The O'Brien Press, Dublin. 1991.

Pawluk Dr.com web page: How can Electromagnetic Fields have an effect on my Body?.

Pert Candace B. Phd. Molecules of Emotion. Why you feel the way you feel. Cox & Wyman, Reading Berkshire. 1997.

Quest Penelope. Self Healing with Reiki. How to create Wholeness, Harmony & Balance for Body, Mind & Spirit. Piatkus. 2003

Radin Dean. The Conscious Universe. Harper One. Barnes Noble. 1997.

Rossi Ernest L. The Psychobiology of Mind-Body Healing: New Concepts of Therapeutic Hypnosis. WW Norton & Co. Inc. New York. 2nd Ed 1994.

Rubik Beverley: The Journal of Alternative & Complimentary Medicine. Dec 2002, 8 (6): 703-717. doi:10.1089/10755530260511711. published in vol 8 issue 6: July 5, 2004.

Samantha-Laughton Dr. M. Punk Science. Inside the Mind of God. O Books. Winchester UK. 2006.

Samantha-Laughton Dr. M. The Genius Groove. The New Science of Creativity. Paradigm Revolution Publishing. UK. 2009.

Sarno John E. MD. The Mind-Body Prescription. Healing The Body, Healing the Pain. Grand Central Life & Style, New York & Boston. First published 1991. 2010.

Waitzkin, H. The Politics of Medical Encounters: How Patients and Doctors deal with Social problems. New Haven, CT: Yale University Press. 1991

Ward Tara. The Healing Handbook. A Spiritual Guide to Healing Yourself and Others. Arcturus Publishing. London. 2008.

Weil Andrew M.D. Spontaneous Healing. How to Discover and Enhance your Body's Natural Ability to Maintain and Heal Itself. Little Brown and Company. London 1995.

Wilson Duff. New Blood Pressure Guidelines pay off for Drug Companies. Seattle Times. June 26-30, cited in Conrad. 2005

Wren Barbara. Cellular Awakening. How you body holds and creates Light. Hay House. London. 2009.

Zubieta Jon-Kar et al. Placebo Effects Mediated by Endogenous Opioid Activity. Journal of Neurosciences. 2005